THE CENTRAL SCHOOL OF SPEECH AND DRAMA
UNIVERSITY OF LONDON

A Har
Clinic

Please return or renew this item by the last date shown.

301

D1609783

A Handbook of Clinical Genetics

J. S. FITZSIMMONS, MB DCH FRCP
Consultant-in-Charge, Trent Sub-Regional Genetic Counselling Service,
City Hospital, Nottingham

with the assistance of

E. M. FITZSIMMONS, RSCN
Nursing Sister, Genetic Counselling Service, City Hospital, Nottingham

WILLIAM HEINEMANN MEDICAL BOOKS LTD · LONDON

William Heinemann Medical Books Ltd
23 Bedford Square
London WC1B 3HH

First published 1980
ISBN 0 433 10530 5

Photoset by D. P. Media Limited
Hitchin, Hertfordshire
Printed in Great Britain by
Redwood Burn Ltd
Trowbridge and Esher

Contents

To our four children and their future

Preface

This text was originally planned for nurses but when completed was also considered to be suitable for medical students and doctors needing an introduction to clinical genetics. There are many more detailed books on the subject available. Most of the clinical material and pedigrees illustrated have been obtained from the counselling service and we are very grateful to all those patients, consultands and families who have attended over the years. We are also grateful to those health visitors and doctors, in particular Dr J. I. McLachlan MB, DCH, DRCOG, who have contributed to the service since its commencement.

Dr P. Cooke, PhD, cytogeneticist, supplied many of the karyotypes and details of liquor amnii analysis. We are particularly indebted to her and her staff for their invaluable help.

Mr A. Bezear, medical artist, and Mr G. B. Gilbert, medical photographer, were responsible for the figures, diagrams and photographic work. We are grateful to them and their colleagues in the Department of Audiovisual Services at the Queen's Medical Centre and City Hospital, Nottingham.

Finally, we wish to thank Mrs H. Barkes who typed the manuscript and coped with the many alterations and additions.

J. S. Fitzsimmons
E. M. Fitzsimmons

1979
Nottingham

1 Introduction

During the past decade doctors and nurses have become aware of the increasing interest in clinical genetics and the growing demand for genetic counselling. This has been the case in most specialities and has benefited the management of many patient problems. For example, paediatric nurses now accept genetic counselling for the families of handicapped children as a helpful and much needed service. The midwife and obstetric staff involved in the expanding field of prenatal diagnosis are already reducing the number of children born with serious abnormalities. In the community the health visitor and the primary health care team dealing with a wide variety of medical and surgical problems recognise the hereditary aspects of many diseases. Finally nursing staff in psychiatric or general medical wards will have to deal with the serious consequences of disorders such as Huntington's Chorea with its familial implications. In all these areas therefore it is possible to appreciate the increasing importance of genetics in everyday nursing and medical practice. It is necessary now to look at why some of these changes have come about. The following factors appear to be important.

Changes in Morbidity and Mortality

There have been significant changes in the causes of morbidity and mortality in childhood over the past half-century. As a result of immunisation children no longer die, or very rarely so, from diseases such as poliomyelitis or diphtheria. Antibiotics have helped to prevent deaths from other infections, and ante-natal care has improved the chances of babies surviving the process of birth. Today death in early infancy and childhood is more likely to be the result of a serious congenital abnormality and although we have no evidence that the number of such abnormalities is increasing they have been highlighted by the reduction in deaths from other causes. In 1975 congenital abnormalities accounted for almost 25 per cent of all stillbirths, 20 per cent of deaths in the first week of life and one in

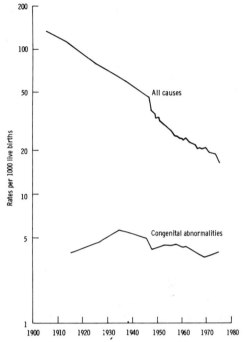

Fig. 1.1   Infant mortality per 1000 live births. Deaths from all causes including congenital abnormalities. England and Wales (After Birth Impairments OHE)

four deaths in the first year of life. Although the infant mortality rate has progressively decreased, the number of deaths from congenital abnormalities has shown little change.

If we now examine the various types of serious congenital abnormalities (Table 1.1), at the top of the list is that group of conditions referred to as neural tube defects and comprising spina bifida, meningomyelocele, anencephaly and some cases of hydrocephalus. The list also includes Down's Syndrome or mongolism and takes account of serious handicapping conditions such as mental retardation, deafness and blindness. By totalling the incidence of these various disorders it can be seen that approximately 25 children per thousand births will suffer from one or more of these serious problems. This is equivalent to 2.5/100 or, more practically, a risk of 1 in 40 of a serious abnormality in any pregnancy. This figure comes as a surprise to many couples and for that reason it is important to put it into perspective. It does also imply a 39 to 1 chance that a child will not have a serious congenital abnormality.

	Approximate Incidence / 1,000 births
Neural Tube Defects	3 - 7
Congenital Heart Disease	6
Severe Mental Retardation	4
Downs Syndrome	1.5
Cleft Lip / Palate	1.5
Talipes	1 - 2
Cerebral Palsy	3
Blindness	0.2
Deafness	0.8
Abnormalities of Limbs	1 - 2
Others including Renal Tract Anomalies	2
	25 - 30

Table 1.1   Incidence of serious congenital abnormalities per 1000 births.

Events are now moving so rapidly that as a result of prenatal diagnosis neural tube abnormalities are becoming less commonly the cause of neo-natal or childhood death. It is now congenital heart disease and kidney abnormalities which are the major causes of death in this period.

There have also been demonstrable changes in mortality and morbidity in adults. Improved social circumstances and antibiotics have helped prevent deaths from conditions such as tuberculosis and other infections. Coronary artery disease, various types of cancer and degenerative disease are now the major problems. In some of these conditions, for example some types of coronary artery disease, the genetic component may be clearly recognised. In others, such as diabetes, hypertension and mental illness, it is more difficult to evaluate the contribution of genetic factors. Nevertheless, genetic disease does provide a considerable addition to the total burden of human illness. Although it is difficult to assess this accurately it has been estimated that if we combine adults and children then about 1 in 10 individuals will have serious genetic disease. Another 1 in 50 will have disease of unknown aetiology probably, to some extent, related to genetic factors.

Fall in Birth Rate

In 1977 there were approximately 600 000 infants born in England and Wales and this is the lowest annual delivery rate since records were introduced. For the first time our population was in negative

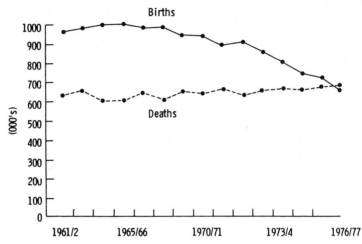

Fig. 1.2   Birth rate and death rate. England and Wales (After Population Trends HMSO)

balance; deaths from all causes outnumbering births. There has been a predicted rise in the birth rate during 1978–1979 due to an increase in the number of women entering the childbearing years. This was the result of the 'baby boom' of the 1960 period but there is no evidence to suggest that it reflects any long term trend.

As a consequence of the fall in the birth rate the average number of children per family has decreased and it is important to note that this trend is not a new one. Records from 1850 show that the decrease has been a steady one and in 1977 the average number of children per family in this country was two or slightly less than two.

Parents rightly wish their children to be born healthy and able to enjoy a normal, active life. Because each child is now more likely to be the result of a planned pregnancy this desire is more often expressed. Fifty years ago with larger families it was not unusual for a child to be born with a serious handicap. Today, such an occurrence is more likely to be seen as preventable and many young couples appear to seek some means of guaranteeing that their children are born healthy and stay that way. Another consequence of fewer pregnancies is that a miscarriage is now a much more significant event and couples may be referred to genetic counselling clinics for advice about some aspects of this problem. As with other conditions it is only possible to give sensible advice if the cause of the miscarriage or stillbirth can be established. It is important therefore to obtain more detailed post-mortem examination of aborted fetuses and stillborn babies.

Advances in Technology and Treatment

Changing patterns of disease in our community have influenced thinking on medical research and practice. There is now more emphasis on the preventative aspects of medicine and health education. However, the prevention of conditions such as Down's Syndrome and spina bifida have had to wait for advances in technology which have become available over this past few years. Increasing experience with amniocentesis and the advent of ultrasound have made prenatal diagnosis possible and safer. In addition there have been significant advances in *cytogenetics*, i.e. the study of chromosomes and their abnormalities. An important landmark in the development of this science was the finding of an extra chromosome in patients with Down's Syndrome. Subsequently changes in the number and structure of chromosomes were demonstrated in other disease states. All of these changes may be identified in a preparation of chromosomes referred to as a *karyotype* and shown in Fig. 1.3.

In the past few years it has been confirmed that there is an increased level of a fetal protein, alpha-fetoprotein, in the amniotic fluid surrounding a fetus with spina bifida or anencephaly. This has made it possible to offer prenatal diagnosis and selective abortion to couples at risk of having a child with this serious abnormality. A

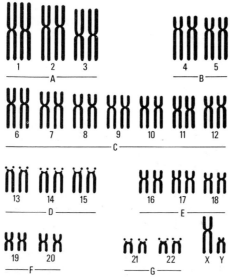

Fig. 1.3 Normal unbanded karyotype. The chromosomes are numbered and grouped according to size. Sex chromosomes bottom right. This is a male.

similar approach is now adopted in a number of rare serious diseases such as the mucopolysaccharidoses. These may result in mental retardation in addition to physical abnormalities. More recently it has become possible to identify fetal blood vessels with the aid of an instrument called a fetoscope. This enables the examiner to sample fetal blood and to make a diagnosis of some genetic diseases, e.g. Duchenne muscular dystrophy and thalassaemia. There is still a fairly high risk associated with this procedure but refinements in the technique and the instruments used are likely to make it safer and more common in the future. Increasing experience with ultrasound should help in the diagnosis of fetal renal cystic disease and possibly also in the detection of abnormalities of head-growth such as microcephaly or hydrocephalus.

Another major stimulus to interest in genetic disease came with the demonstration that children born with phenylketonuria could develop normally, provided they were commenced on a suitable diet in the newborn period. In this recessively inherited disease affected children have a deficiency of an enzyme and cannot metabolise the phenylalanine present in a normal diet. As a consequence of this they may be mentally retarded. This biochemical disease is not yet preventable but like other diseases has now been shown to be treatable. Research may well show that other genetic diseases may be treatable in the same way.

Complex Social Changes

In recent times the liberalisation of the laws on abortion and improved techniques of contraception have, in addition to reducing the birth rate, obviously allowed women much more freedom than was possible in the past. This has meant their involvement in professions and other jobs which would have been denied them had they to care for children. The burden of caring for a handicapped child is usually more the responsibility of mother than father. It is understandable, therefore, that many women today would wish to avoid such restrictions on their freedom.

In addition to changes in the law there have been some more subtle changes. Today, there is less pressure from parents on young couples to have children. There is also less pressure from society and an only child is not considered to be such a tragedy as was the case in the past. Many couples today elect not to have any children, and one of the reasons given for this is the increasing cost of rearing a child in times of 'inflation'. Politicians and the media frequently suggest that all of us have higher expectations. It is difficult to define exactly what this means but undoubtedly the need for individual fulfilment is now more frequently discussed than was the case a generation ago. There is an increasing demand for more leisure time and an acceptance that this applies to women as well as men. The divorce rate has increased and marriage is no longer considered the necessary consequence of two people wanting to live together.

Over the years there has been a steady increase in demand by the public for more information about disease and its consequences. It is difficult to be sure of the real reasons for this but the media, particularly television, appear to have played a large part in stimulating the public to question medical opinion. This, in many cases, has meant that doctors and nurses have to spend more time discussing patient problems. It would seem reasonable that parents of a seriously handicapped child would want to know why this had happened and would also want to know the chances of it happening again. Assessing the recurrence risk of an abnormality and attempting to answer the questions raised is a large part of the rapidly growing field of *genetic counselling*. This new addition to standard medical practice seems to have resulted from all the factors so far discussed, coupled with the demand of our patients for more information. We will see, however, that it is not sufficient to compute a risk for a particular condition; it is also the responsibility of the genetic nurse and doctor to ensure that this information is understood and is imparted in a sympathetic manner.

2

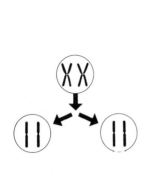

Genetic and Environmental Factors in Disease

Having outlined some of the reasons for the increasing interest in genetic counselling it is necessary to identify those disorders in which this type of advice and information is relevant.

Reference has already been made to the large number of children born every year with a serious congenital abnormality. In many cases the cause of the abnormality is not apparent but in others, specific causative factors can be identified. These may be divided into two major groups – genetic and environmental. Today, the study of congenital anomalies and their causes, the science of *teratology*, is an expanding field. There is a constant search for those agents, *teratogens*, which produce abnormalities of growth or formation of organs in the fetus.

Environmental Factors

Infection with rubella in the first trimester of pregnancy is known to be the cause of a number of serious abnormalities in the fetus including mental retardation, cataracts and deafness. Other infecting organisms which can produce fetal damage are cytomegalovirus and the protozoon responsible for toxoplasmosis. Both may produce hydrocephalus and mental retardation. Some drugs administered to mother in the early stages of pregnancy have been shown to be the cause of a small number of abnormalities, about 5 per cent of the total. Thalidomide is the most quoted example but this drug is no longer in use and we must now examine other commonly used drugs for possible ill effects. Steroids are known to cause changes in the genitalia of female infants; the anti-convulsant, Epanutin, may be related to hare-lip abnormalities and oestrogens contained in the 'pill' if taken in early pregnancy may possibly produce ill effects. More recently it has been recognised that excessive intake of alcohol by mother may cause intellectual retardation and some minor physical anomalies in her infant. Some antimetabolites have also been shown to be teratogenic. It is obvious we have managed to identify only very few environmental factors causing congenital abnormalities.

Genetic Factors

In other infants it is apparent that an inherited factor has been largely responsible for the condition and the transmission of the disease from mother or father to their offspring may be very obvious. A good example is Marfan's Syndrome in which one or other parent has long thin fingers and toes (arachnodactyly). In addition such patients are at increased risk of rupture of the aorta and many have dislocation of the lens. Each child born to such a parent has a high risk of inheriting the abnormal gene which causes the condition. In this situation it is genetic factors and not the environment which is producing the teratogenic effect. This is not to suggest that genes work in isolation. A person's ultimate physical development is the result of the interaction between genetic inheritance, the intrauterine environment and subsequent postuterine environment. This is an important basic principle of genetics, and nature (genes) and nurture (environment) cannot easily be separated. Nevertheless, there are a considerable number of diseases in which an hereditary factor or genetic effect is more important and such diseases are referred to as *single gene* or *unifactorial* disorders. Examples are tuberose sclerosis, achondroplasia, haemophilia and muscular dystrophy. In some of these the disease is clearly transmitted from generation to generation, whereas in others the hereditary background is only recognised when more than one affected child is born to normal parents. Another group of conditions, usually without a familial background but nevertheless due to disordered gene function, result from chromosomal abnormalities. Whereas genes, normal or abnormal, cannot be seen by any current means, it is possible to demonstrate abnormalities of chromosomes by examining a karyotype. This may reveal alterations in either their number or their structure. One of the most common examples of a chromosomal abnormality is Down's Syndrome or mongolism. In this disease there is an additional chromosome and this can be shown to be an extra No. 21. Normally there are only two of each numbered pair but in Down's Syndrome there are three of pair 21. This is referred to as *trisomy 21*.

The total number of patients born with chromosomal abnormalities is small, probably only about 1 per cent of live births. However, it has been shown by examination of material from early miscarriages that a considerable proportion, probably as high as 30 per cent, of aborted fetuses have some form of chromosomal abnormality. In some this is due to the loss of chromosomal material, e.g. Turner's Syndrome, in which there is only one X chromosome instead of the usual two. In others the total number of chromosomes may be doubled or trebled, a condition referred to as *polyploidy*. The placenta from such fetuses may be larger than usual and this may give a clue to the underlying cause. In single gene defects it is an alteration in the quality of gene action which seems to be the important factor. In chromosomal disorders with many genes involved the clinical abnormalities are the result of quantitative changes.

There are other diseases which may afflict members of a family more often than could be accounted for by chance. In these it is assumed that there is a genetic factor which produces a predisposition to the disease, but some additional environmental agent is also necessary for its production. These are referred to as *multifactorial* diseases and the genetic component is thought to be the result of a combination of numerous genes, i.e. a polygenic effect. Unfortunately, this group contains many common diseases such as spina bifida, club feet and some form of heart disease. In addition it also includes major health problems affecting adults such as diabetes and probably schizophrenia.

In some conditions twin studies may be useful in deciding the relative importance of genetic or environmental factors. Twins are of two kinds, identical or *monozygotic* and non-identical or *dizygotic*. Identical twins have the same genetic constitution because they result from the division of a single fertilised ovum. Non-identical twins are no more alike than ordinary brothers and sisters. Diseases due entirely to genetic factors should affect both identical twins. They are said to be *concordant*. Diseases due to environmental factors should normally not affect either monozygotic or dizygotic twins more often than singleton births. In this situation they are said to be *discordant*. When both environmental and genetic factors are at work the degree of concordance will reflect the genetic contribution; a high concordance rate suggesting that heredity is more important than the environment.

Finally, a number of **developmental defects** without any obvious cause, may be shown in future to be at least partly the result of genetic action. A great deal of further research is necessary to elucidate the many possible factors that may disturb normal growth and development of the human embryo.

Despite the increasing number of diseases now recognised to be of genetic origin there are considerable difficulties in assessing accurately the part played by hereditary factors in the overall burden of human illness. As we have seen, in some disorders the genetic component may be very obvious. Hereditary diseases affecting successive generations in a family have been recognised for many centuries and are recorded in the earliest medical literature. In other disorders, however, where the genetic contribution may be less obvious or where the disease does not produce clinical manifestations until later in life, the hereditary aspects may be easily overlooked. This is even more likely today with small families and with the increasing tendency for families to disperse more widely than was the case in the past. In some villages and rural areas however it may still be possible to observe hereditary factors at work. For this reason the community nurse and general practitioner may be able to anticipate specific diseases because of their knowledge of particular families. There are now between 1000 and 2000 disorders known to be the result of faulty gene action and many more in which genes may play a major role. Some surveys of the prevalence of genetic diseases in the community have been reported but much more detailed information is required. In the 1960s a survey from Northern Ireland suggested that 26 per cent of the occupants of all institutional beds, 6 per cent of all consultations with general practitioners and 8 per cent of those with hospital consultants, were patients suffering from genetically determined disease. More recently in England and North America it has been reported that as many as 30 per cent of all paediatric admissions to children's units are the result of genetic or congenital disease. A recent study of an American adult medical unit revealed that approximately 13 per cent of the patients had illnesses resulting from hereditary factors.

There is little doubt, therefore, that genetic disease is a major cause of death and chronic ill health. In order to plan health services for the future it is essential to have information about the incidence of such diseases and their distribution in various regions and populations. There is an obvious need to monitor accurately serious birth defects and to detect early any changes in the frequency or pattern of malformations. Unfortunately there is an increasing number of drugs prescribed to women in the first trimester of pregnancy when the fetus is at maximum risk. Some of these drugs may be teratogenic and thalidomide is a good example. Following its introduction to the British market it was frequently used in the management of vomiting in early pregnancy. Despite sporadic reports of its possible role in the

production of limb abnormalities in the fetus, a large number of infants were affected before it was eventually withdrawn from use.
More recently it has been reported that the anticoagulant, Warfarin, may be teratogenic and the infant in Fig. 2.1 demonstrates the abnormalities which may be seen. There is shortening of the limbs, a depressed nasal bridge and an odd-looking face. The patient has a congenital heart lesion and cataracts. The most characteristic finding however is stippled calcification at the growing ends of the long bones. This combination of abnormalities is referred to as Conradi's Syndrome. In common with some other conditions it may result from either environmental or, on occasions, genetic factors. Although rare it has occurred in more than one child in some families suggesting recessive inheritance. In others, as mentioned, it has been reported following the ingestion of Warfarin by mother early in pregnancy. A disease which results from an environmental agent but which is very similar to that resulting from genetic factors is called a *phenocopy*. It is interesting also that disease resulting from genetic

Fig. 2.1   Conradi's Disease. Striking physical appearance. May be caused by genetic or environmental factors.

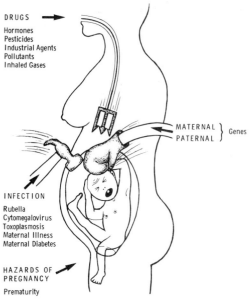

DRUGS
Hormones
Pesticides
Industrial Agents
Pollutants
Inhaled Gases

MATERNAL
PATERNAL } Genes

INFECTION
Rubella
Cytomegalovirus
Toxoplasmosis
Maternal Illness
Maternal Diabetes

HAZARDS OF
PREGNANCY
Prematurity

Fig. 2.2   The fetus has to survive a variety of insults and dangers. Fortunately the majority do so!

factors alone may have different modes of inheritance and this is referred to as genetic *heterogeneity*. The disease may be transmitted in a dominant, recessive or sex-linked fashion. However this does not necessarily imply that they are all the same disease, only that the physical abnormalities produced are similar. For example, there is a variety of Conradi's Disease which is dominantly inherited and is milder than the recessively inherited variety.

Industry now uses many dangerous chemicals and these may pollute the atmosphere or foodstuffs. A number of them are known to be capable of producing changes in genes, referred to as *mutations*. Some of these may be responsible for human diseases and in future other chemicals may be shown to have a similar mutagenic effect.

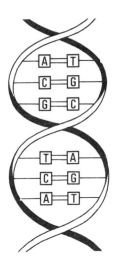

3
The Genetic Code

To appreciate how faulty gene action may result in disease it is necessary to review briefly our current understanding of the mechanism of inheritance. As described here the process is grossly simplified but is essentially such a fascinating one that it is worth some effort to try and understand the basic principles.

The human body is composed of millions of cells of various types comprising different tissues and organs. For these cells to perform their individual functions and to reproduce themselves it is obvious that somewhere in the cell must be stored the information necessary for the manufacture of the individual cellular components. It is essential that as the cells mature and begin to degenerate so they must ensure that a new generation of cells is available and able to continue their work. In the larger context an individual has to produce germ cells, ova or sperm, containing the information necessary for the continuity of the species. It is now recognised that the majority of this information is stored in chemical form in the nucleus of the cell and is contained within the chromosomes in the form of genes. There is some evidence that the cytoplasm in some species may also contain genetic information. However, it is within the chromosomes that the majority of the coded instruction is located.

Earlier we saw how chromosomes may be arranged in neatly matched pairs to make up a karyotype. Normally they are not visible in the resting cell nucleus and arc not present in the same form as we see them in the karyotype. Instead they are single stranded, inextricably coiled in the nucleus and individual chromosomes cannot be

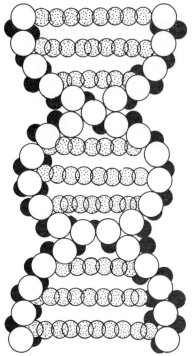

Fig. 3.1   The DNA molecule.

identified. However, when cell division commences the single stranded chromosomes condense, thicken and become more easily seen under the microscope. At a certain stage in the division they split into two, remaining attached at a junction point referred to as the centromere. It is at this stage that further chromosome division is halted when a karyotype is being prepared and a karyotype is, therefore, a preparation of chromosomes as they appear during the activity involved in nuclear division.

The strands of each divided chromosome are referred to as *chromatids* and the ability of the chromosome to replicate itself in this way is an essential requirement for subsequent cell division. In all body or somatic cells (soma = body) the total chromosome number is 46, 23 matching pairs, composed of a chromosome from each parent. 22 of these pairs are similar in males and females and are called *autosomes*, the remaining pair are the *sex chromosomes*. In the female these consist of two equal X chromosomes, but in the male there is only a single X and a much smaller Y.

When a normal body cell, be it skin, bone or muscle, divides it does

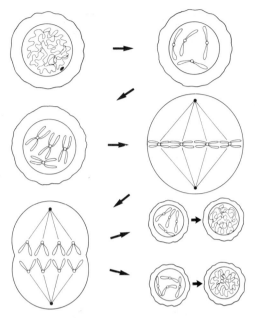

Fig. 3.2a   Mitosis: somatic cell division. Each daughter cell has the same complement of chromosomes as the parent cell. The figure shows resting cell (top left) through to daughter cells in resting phase (bottom right). Two pairs of chromosomes only are depicted.

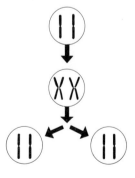

Fig. 3.2b   Mitosis 'Like father like son'. Chromosome number in offspring as in parent.

so by a process called *mitosis* and in this process individual chromosomes divide longitudinally, one half passing to each daughter cell. In each half there is an exact replica of the genes of the parent chromosome. Each new cell therefore contains the same 23 pairs of chromosomes and hence the same complement of genes as the original parent cell. However, the ova or sperm, referred to as the *gametes*, must contain only half the total number of chromosomes. Subsequently at fertilisation, when ovum and sperm combine to form the *zygote* or new individual, the total chromosomal complement is again reconstituted. As a consequence of these two different processes, therefore, the body can maintain its activities and ensure the continuity of the species.

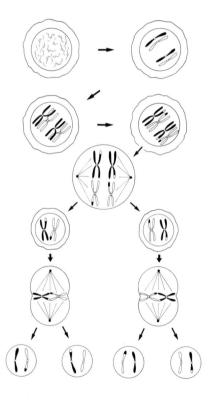

Fig. 3.3a   Meiosis: formation of gametes, ova and sperm, with half the number of chromosomes of parent cell. Two pairs of chromosomes only shown.

Fig. 3.3b The 'melting pot'. Cross-over ensures a mix of genes. The exchange of genetic material between homologous chromosomes.

In the formation of the gametes a different type of cellular division is necessary and this is called *meiosis*. Individual chromosomes do not divide in the same way as in mitosis but each complete member of a pair passes to the daughter cell to form the gamete. In this way the ovum or sperm contains only the *haploid* number of chromosomes, i.e. half the total number, 23. Cells containing the full complement of chromosomes, i.e. 46, are referred to as *diploid*. Although the separation of the chromosomes at meiosis allows for considerable diversity in the gametes of an individual, another process called crossing-over ensures further mixes of genes from both parents. This is seen in Fig. 3.3b and demonstrates that during meiosis when a pair of matched or *homologous* chromosomes lie together, segments of one chromosome cross over and join with the chromosomes from the other parent.

It is possible to demonstrate that chromosomes are composed of a specific nucleic acid, deoxyribonucleic acid (DNA) and protein. Another nucleic acid, ribonucleic acid (RNA), is also present in the nucleus in small quantities but the majority is in the cytoplasm of the cell. The DNA molecule is composed of a large number of smaller chemical units called nucleotides and for this reason is referred to as a polynucleotide. It has a very special type of construction because it can be shown to be double stranded and these two strands are twisted on one another to form a spiral referred to as the double helix. Each strand of the spiral is made up of hundreds of nucleotides and each nucleotide consists of a sugar, a phosphate and a base arranged in a linear fashion along the DNA molecule. The strands are held together by the bases and the total arrangement may be likened to a coiled rope ladder. The two sides of the ladder are composed of the sugar and phosphate while the rungs of the ladder are made up of the bases. There are four of these, adenine, guanine, cytosine and thiamine. Because of their special characteristics one base will never pair with the like base and the combination is therefore always adenine with thiamine and cytosine with guanine. The fact that there are four different bases means there can be four different nucleotides, each consisting of phosphate, a sugar and a base. It has been further shown that in terms of function these nucleotide bases are arranged in groups of three. Such a group,

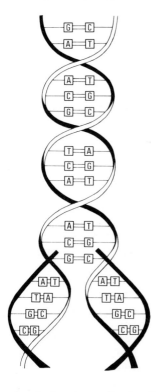

fig. 3.4   DNA molecule showing replication. The new daughter molecules are an exact replica of the original.

determining the structure of one amino-acid, is called a *codon*. Because three bases code for one amino-acid and there are four bases in total, this allows for 64 possible combinations, more than sufficient for the 20 amino-acids required to form body proteins. It is proteins which are the end result of all genetic action.

With this basic information we may now define a gene as a sequence of nucleotide bases, perhaps as many as 500, but still only a small proportion of the total DNA molecule. Because it is impossible to see specific genes it is difficult to estimate the exact length of the DNA molecule which they occupy. However, the exact location of the gene on the chromosome is important and is referred to as the *gene locus*. Such a gene locus will specify the information necessary for the formation of a particular amino-acid, e.g. phenylalanine, leucine, valine or tyrosine depending on the arrangement of the bases. A group of amino-acids in turn will produce a specific protein or enzyme. This particular sequence of events, i.e. the manufacture of protein or enzymes from the coded information in the genes, forms the basis of inherited characteristics. In situations where the information is incorrectly coded, hereditary disease may result.

We must now look at how a portion of DNA, which we have defined as a gene, coded for a specific amino-acid, is to be translated into the finished product. Proteins are eventually manufactured not in the nucleus but in the cytoplasm of the cell. There has, therefore, to be some means available whereby the information located in the DNA within the nucleus is subsequently transported into the body of the cell. It is at this stage that the ribonucleic acid (RNA) plays a part. During cell activity when the essential cellular components are to be produced, decoding of the stored information on the DNA molecule commences. It is assumed that the two strands of DNA separate at the appropriate point for a specific sequence of gene information to be copied. This information is probably available from one strand only. By this process of separation one strand of DNA contains bases which are no longer aligned with the appropriate bases on the other strand. At this stage the other nucleic acid, RNA, which is single stranded, aligns itself with the appropriate bases on the free strand of DNA. There have to be enzymes and energy available for this process to take place. The RNA molecule is also composed of four bases, adenine, guanine and cytosine but uracil is present in place of DNA thiamine. As before, guanine pairs with cytosine but adenine pairs with uracil instead of thiamine. RNA is also arranged in codons, a succession of three bases, as is DNA. We now have the genetic message from the DNA coded on to a slightly different material, the RNA, and this RNA is referred to as messenger RNA (mRNA). This process is referred to as *transcription*. The blueprint is unaltered but it is now transportable and this mRNA is capable of carrying the message from the nucleus to the cytoplasm for further development. In the cytoplasm the RNA becomes associated with groups of small particles called *ribosomes*. During this process the RNA combines with another type of nucleic acid present in the cytoplasm called transfer RNA (tRNA). The function of tRNA is to transfer amino-acids with which it is associated to their appropriate places on the mRNA template in the ribosomes. Where the base sequences on the mRNA template specify specific amino-acids such as leucine or valine so these are supplied by the tRNA. The eventual protein formed will depend on the varying combination of amino-acids. In this situation tRNA behaves like a builders merchant supplying the materials as dictated by the builder's plans. The original architect's drawings were supplied at a particular location on the DNA molecule in the nucleus. This very complicated process, therefore, terminates with the formation of a chain of amino-acids which eventually link to form a specific protein. Different cells will produce different proteins necessary for their function but how individual chromosomes elect to be responsible for cell differentiation is unknown.

A number of questions will immediately spring to mind, e.g. How does the decoding process start? How does it stop? An even more basic question might be, how was the total information in the correct sequence to start with? There appears to be a specific sequence of

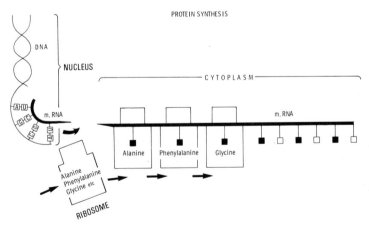

Fig. 3.5   Protein synthesis. In the nucleus the mRNA takes up the code from a strand of DNA. It carries this to the cytoplasm where protein is eventually produced.

nucleotides, a codon, which does not code for any specific amino-acid but instead acts as a starter mechanism. The activation of this group of nucleotides seems to be the stimulus for decoding to take place. Another sequence of nucleotides acts as a stop mechanism terminating the decoding process. There seem, therefore, to be some genes which have a structural role producing protein or enzymes and some which have only a regulatory function. More recently it has also been recognised that genes themselves may be split into smaller pieces and a sequence of gene information may be discontinuous. It is assumed that the code has been built up very gradually from early primitive life forms and as a result of the evolutionary change will continue to alter over the next millions of years. The change is slow and individual genes may have a half-life of a million years between any significant alteration in their structure. We do not know how genes bring about their effects. We know the DNA molecule is combined with other proteins in the chromosome but we do not know exactly how these are arranged. It seems likely that the DNA molecule is tightly coiled within the chromosome but it is difficult to see how decoding can start in such a situation. However, there has to be a mechanism and obviously we have much to learn about this fascinating process.

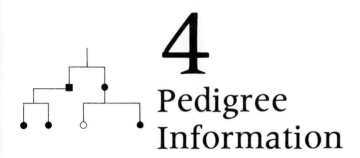

4

Pedigree
Information

To demonstrate how disease may be transmitted from parents to
their offspring or in some cases to show the familial nature of various
disorders it is necessary to compile a family history or pedigree. This
is an important task for the doctor or nurse involved in genetic
counselling. Fig. 4.1 lists the symbols currently used for this purpose.
The male and female symbols vary. The square and circle are more
commonly used but the circle with an arrow or cross is still preferred
by some. In extensive family pedigrees it may become impossible to
fit all the members of successive generations into a vertical pedigree.
In these circumstances the family tree may be drawn in oval or
circular form. For most purposes, however, the form of the pedigree
shown in the figures is adequate.

Roman numerals denote the generations and Arabic numerals
specify the number of persons in that generation. In the pedigree in
Fig. 4.2 the arrow indicates a male, No. 4 in generation III, who is
the person attending the genetic counselling clinic for advice and
referred to as the consultand or counsellee. It would be incorrect to
refer to him as a patient if he does not suffer from any particular
disease. These terms are somewhat clumsy and in some cases it may
be sufficient to refer to the person by name. An arrow may also
indicate a proband or propositus implying that this is the person who
has directed our attention to the family pedigree. It could, for
example, be a child with Down's Syndrome. In addition to helping
clarify how some disorders are transmitted, a properly taken family
pedigree has other advantages. It may, for example, aid in the
diagnosis of some diseases. In the pedigree shown the man aged 35
presented with psychiatric symptoms for which his physician could
find no satisfactory explanation. The problem was solved when
details of the family history were obtained and it was learned that his
mother died at the age of 55 years from Huntington's Chorea. As a
consequence of the family's involvement with a genetic counsellor

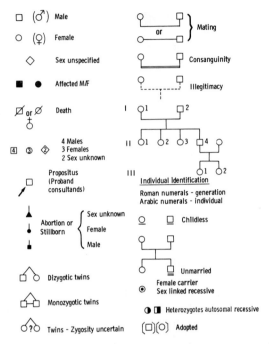

Fig. 4.1 Symbols used in pedigrees. Where necessary it is legitimate to make up some special ones – provided the key is supplied. Sibs are recorded eldest to the left and in a mating some prefer to place the male first.

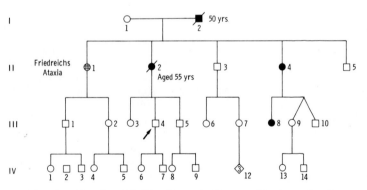

Fig. 4.2 Family with Huntington's Chorea. The consultand is marked with an arrow. When the pedigree details were obtained his illness was diagnosed. His aunt's illness had been misdiagnosed. She did not suffer from Friedreich's Ataxia.

another relative, the consultand's aunt, whose illness had been diagnosed as possibly some form of Friedreich's Ataxia, was also found to suffer from Huntington's Chorea. This diagnosis only became obvious when the family complaint was uncovered and a proper pedigree obtained.

It soon becomes apparent to the nurse or doctor in the genetic counselling clinic that the majority of family histories in standard hospital records are inadequate for counselling purposes. They rarely extend beyond one generation and frequently lack any family information whatsoever. Clearly this could, on occasions, make a diagnosis more difficult and on other occasions may actively delay the treatment of a genetic disease. In the pedigree in Fig. 4.3, Mrs C. had given birth to a male infant who subsequently died at the age of three months from galactosaemia. This is a fatal recessively inherited biochemical disorder characterised in infancy by failure to thrive, congenital cataracts and enlargement of the liver. It is treatable by the elimination of lactose from the diet and provided this is commenced early enough the outlook may be reasonable. The disease is inherited but because there was a gap of 15 years between the birth of this affected child and her next pregnancy she made little reference to it before delivery. The obstetric records did show that a previous infant had died but there had been no reference to the cause of his death. Following a miscarriage the second affected baby was born and became unwell early in life. There was a delay in making the diagnosis and in instituting proper treatment.

These examples could be repeated many times but hopefully with increasing awareness of the importance of clinical genetics more

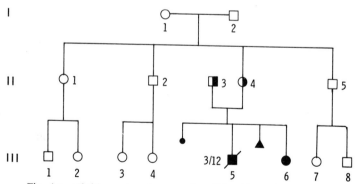

Fig. 4.3   Child number 6 generation III suffered from galactosaemia. A previous child had died from the same disease. Both parents heterozygous for responsible gene. Mother also had two miscarriages.

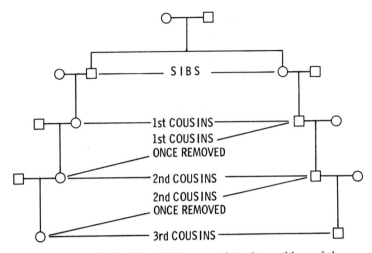

Fig. 4.4   Relationships. Helps to explain the problem of the
second cousin once removed!

attention will be paid to taking a proper family history. The
identification and selection of families with hereditary disease is
referred to as *ascertainment*.

Many members of the public show a considerable interest in their
family background and geneology is a popular pastime in many
countries. Most of us like to have knowledge of our basic roots and
most individuals attending a genetic counselling clinic can with
encouragement produce extremely detailed, and on occasions, artis-
tic pedigrees! However, it is necessary to be familiar with the terminology which may be used. Some consultands might expect the
nurse to immediately understand the relationship of 'second cousin
Hilda once removed on mother's side!'

Relationships are demonstrated in Fig. 4.4.

It is also in order to refer to degrees of relationship.
First degree relatives (1°) are parent and child or sib and sib.
Second degree relatives (2°) are uncles, aunts, nephews and nieces.
Third degree relatives (3°) are first cousins.

5
Inheritance Patterns

We must now move from looking at genes on a chemical level to consider how gene action may be responsible for our inherited characteristics and, on occasions, disease. As we have seen, a person inherits a chromosome from each parent and these chromosomes contain a specific number of genes. In the same way that the chromosomes are paired so an individual gene from one parent has its equivalent from the other parent. These equivalent forms of a gene are referred to as *alleles* and if they are alike, producing the same end result, the individual is referred to as *homozygous* for those genes. If they are dissimilar, even if not producing any obvious clinical effect, the person is said to be *heterozygous*. Minor differences in genes are common and allow for the wide diversity of many human characteristics. The eventual expression of this gene action will cause a different physical, biochemical and physiological make-up in each individual. This is referred to as a person's *phenotype* which is the result of the interaction between his genetic make-up, his *genotype*, and the environment. It is important to stress that a defective gene in one chromosome will produce an entirely different effect from a faulty gene in another chromosome.

Genes cannot be seen, but as we have learned, the position of a specific gene on a chromosome is referred to as the gene locus. It has been possible to plot the position or loci of some genes on specific chromosomes. This is called gene mapping and is of considerable interest in genetic research.

If, in the way we have discussed, a person inherits two genes, one the allele of the other but one of which is abnormal, then certain consequences may follow. If the altered or mutated gene results in some observable change or disease, despite the presence of the normal allele then the effect of this gene is said to be *dominant* to that of the normal one. Disease produced in this way is said to be dominantly inherited.

If, on the other hand, the abnormal gene fails to produce any phenotypic abnormalities or disease its effects are said to be *recessive* to those of the normal allele. In many cases it may be impossible to demonstrate any effect of this abnormal gene. However, if a person inherits such a similar defective gene from both parents then the combined effect of these two genes may be to produce specific disease. Abnormalities produced in this way are said to be recessively inherited. It should be apparent that the difference between these two modes of inheritance is only one of degree. If we had more sensitive methods of detecting the effects of genes then it would be possible to demonstrate the effects of a gene whether it produced disease or not. As we shall see this is already possible in some recessively inherited conditions.

Most genes are located on chromosomes other than the sex chromosome; these are the autosomes and disease resulting from abnormal genes located on these chromosomes is referred to as *autosomal disease*. The sex chromosomes, however, also contain genes and these may be capable of producing abnormalities. This is *sex-linked disease*. So far there does not seem to be any abnormal gene located on the Y chromosome causing serious abnormalities. For that reason most sex-linked disease is referred to as X-linked, since the larger X chromosome seems to be the one usually carrying the gene at fault.

A gene which is abnormal as a result of a change in its structure is said to have mutated and disease resulting from the action of such a gene is referred to as *unifactorial* or *Mendelian*. It is presumed that such a single gene is capable of producing a major effect. Other genes, with much less effect, will only produce clinical manifestations if they act in combination. Our conception of a single gene causing disease in this way stems from the work of a monk, Gregor Mendel, in the 19th century. The conclusions he reached resulted from his experiments with the common garden pea. Although there have been important contributions to our understanding of inheritance since that time, his original conclusions are still of great practical value in the management of patient problems.

As has been discussed disease in man thought to be genetic in origin may be divided into three major groups. Those diseases resulting from the action of a single major gene, those due to abnormalities of the chromosomes and therefore, multiple genes, and those in which genes and environmental factors work in conjunction. Some other developmental disorders may well have a genetic basis but so far this has not been identified. We must now examine each of these modes of inheritance in more detail.

Single Gene (Unifactorial) Inheritance

When the abnormal gene responsible for a disease is located on an autosome then the mode of inheritance is said to be autosomal and it may be dominant or recessive.

Autosomal Dominant Inheritance

A large number of conditions, over 1000, result from the action of abnormal genes transmitted in this way. Although they are individually rare, most having a frequency of less than 1 in 5000, they are important because of their total number and because they may present very striking clinical features. Table 5.1 lists some of the more common dominantly inherited disorders. The severity of most of these conditions varies considerably.

* Achondroplasia
  Amylodosis (Type 1)
* Anorectal Anomalies - some types
  Aperts Syndrome
* Brachydactyly
* Cataracts
* Charcot - Marie tooth disease
  Chorea - Hereditary Benign
* Clinodactyly
  Corneal Dystrophy
  Ectodermal Dysplasia
* Ehlers - Danlos Syndrome
  Englemann Disease
  Familial Mediterranean Fever
* Haemangiomata
* Hernia - Inguinal, bilateral
  Holt - Oram Syndrome
* Huntingtons Chorea
* Hyperlipldaemia Type II
  Iris Hypoplasia + Glaucoma
  Keratosis Hands + Feet (Tylosis)
  Klippel - Feil Deformity + Deafness
* Lentigines
  Lymphoedema with Yellow Nails
* Marfans Syndrome
* Migraine (Familial)

Multiple Exostoses
* Myotonic Dystrophy
  Nail - Patella Syndrome
  Narcolepsy
* Neurofibromatosis
  Noonans Syndrome
  Optic Atrophy (Congenital)
* Osteogenisis Imperfecta
* Polycystic Kidneys
* Polydactyly
* Polyposis Coli (Peutz Syndrome)
  Porphyria
  Retinal Aplasia
* Retinitis Pigmentosa
  Retinoblastoma
* Sickle cell trait
  Spherocytosis
* Split - Hand Deformity
  Stein - Levanthal Syndrome
* Syndactyly
  Treacher - Collins Syndrome
* Tuberose Sclerosis
  Ullrich - Noonan Syndrome
  Van der Woudes Syndrome
* Von - Willebrands Disease
* Wardenburgs Syndrome

*more frequent occurrence

Table 5.1   Dominantly inherited disorders. The more common ones are marked.

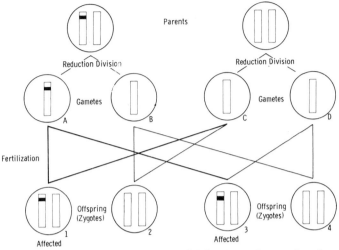

Fig. 5.1 Possible outcome at fertilisation. One pair of chromosomes only shown in each parent. The affected parent carries the abnormal gene (black line) and manifests the disorder. At reduction division some gametes (A) also carry this abnormal gene and some do not. At fertilisation the zygote with this gene will develop the disease. The risk is 50/50 for each pregnancy.

Fig. 5.1 demonstrates the transmission of an abnormal gene carried by one of a pair of autosomes and resulting in clinical disease. The patient carrying the abnormal gene and one normal allele in the other chromosome is referred to as a heterozygote. In dominantly inherited disease either sex may be affected. Because an individual contributes only one of the two chromosomes carrying the abnormal gene to the gamete, then each offspring has a 50 per cent or 1 in 2 chance of inheriting the abnormal gene and hence manifesting the disease. It is important to remember that this risk remains the same for each successive pregnancy, irrespective of the outcome of the preceding one. With relatively large families it may be that the total of affected and unaffected children will approximate to 50/50 but with the smaller human family all may be affected or, with luck, unaffected.

As in many other forms of disease, irrespective of their cause, the severity of the condition may vary considerably from one individual to another. In clinical genetics this variation is referred to as *expressivity* and stresses the importance of examining patients thoroughly before declaring them free of the disease. Some of those affected may have only minor manifestations but by passing on the

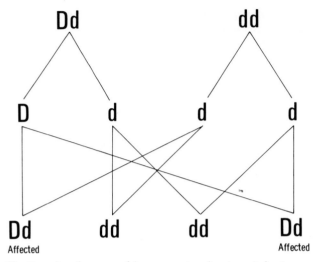

Fig. 5.2 Another way of demonstrating dominant inheritance. Each person carrying a 'single dose' of gene D will develop the disease; d is the normal allele.

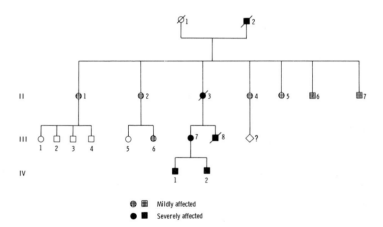

Fig. 5.3 Von Recklinghausen's Disease (neurofibromatosis). The woman 3 in generation II died from malignant change in a lesion in her spine. The male 8 in generation III died from a cerebral tumour. Both boys in generation IV were severely affected and one of them had developed hydrocephalus due to the position of one of the neurofibromata.

responsible gene may produce a child with a more serious form of the disease. The reason for this variation in gene action is unknown. Most dominantly inherited diseases, with a few exceptions such as Huntington's Chorea, show considerable variation in their clinical severity. This is demonstrated in Fig. 5.3. This is a pedigree of a family in which many members are affected by neurofibromatosis or Von Recklinghausen's Disease. This disorder is characterised by patches of pigmentation in the skin, the so-called café-au-lait spots, and by tumours, fibromata, of nerve fibres. Some of these may be sufficiently large to cause obvious swellings and some may even be pedunculated and hang like grapes from the skin. Others because of their position may produce very serious symptoms of compression, for example, in the spinal cord or in the brain. This family demonstrates a wide spectrum of severity with the least affected having only café-au-lait spots while others have the typical fibromata. Some demonstrate a further complication, malignant degeneration in the tumours.

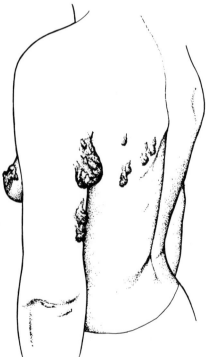

Fig. 5.4   The skin lesions of neurofibromatosis. The unsightly appearance may have profound psychological implications.

The importance of recognising varying clinical expression of genetic disease cannot be over-stressed. The nurse involved in this work will very soon become familiar with this characteristic of gene action. In some families various types of dominantly inherited disease may affect the offspring of parents who appear completely normal. In such situations it is thought that the abnormal gene is not present in the somatic or body cells of the parents and hence does not produce disease in them. However, the mutated gene is present in their gametes, either the ovum or sperm, and in this way can obviously be passed to the offspring. The end result will be the same as if one of the parents had the disease. The affected child will now have the same risk of passing on the abnormal gene as any other affected person. Achondroplasia is a good example of the inheritance of a new mutation; as many as 80 per cent of all achondroplastics have normal parents.

Finally, it does occasionally happen that a genetic disorder present in one generation fails to appear in the next but reappears in subsequent generations. This is not a common occurrence and may well only highlight our inability to detect minor clinical effects of the abnormal gene. In these circumstances the gene is said to lack *penetrance*. It has failed to produce any demonstrable evidence of the disease. This is difficult to explain on our current understanding of gene action and these so-called skip generations are less frequently reported today than in the past. This may be a reflection of more thorough clinical examination of our patients. On occasions disease transmitted in a dominant fashion may appear at a younger age in affected persons in successive generations. This is referred to as *anticipation*. It may be a consequence of earlier diagnosis rather than any alteration in the gene expression.

Although the concept of single gene inheritance is a useful one and of practical value it should not hide the fact that it is too simple an approach and gene action may be modified by many factors. The environment is obviously important and genes do not work in isolation. Their clinical expression will depend on many factors.

Summary of Characteristics of Autosomal Dominant Inheritance
1. Normally an affected person has an affected parent, with the exception of the new mutation.
2. Affected persons have, on average, affected and normal offspring in equal proportion.
3. Normal children of an affected parent usually have only normal offspring.
4. There may be considerable variation in the clinical severity of the disease and both sexes may be affected.

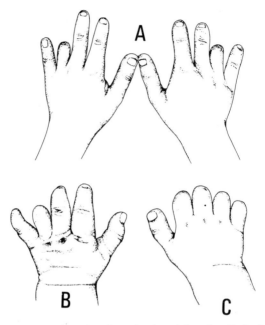

Fig. 5.5   A. Mother's hands: reduction deformity; B. 1st born infant: same severity of deformity; C. 2nd born infant: much more serious deformity. This demonstrates varying expressivity clearly.

Autosomal Recessive Inheritance

More than 500 disorders result from this type of inheritance. Whereas some autosomal dominant disease tends to produce clinically striking abnormalities, some recessively inherited disorders may more commonly result in biochemical disturbance. In some instances this may be a single enzyme deficiency which may be so severe as to produce mental retardation, for example in phenylketonuria, or gross disturbance in fluid balance as in the adrenogenital syndrome.

Cystic fibrosis is the most common of the autosomal recessively inherited disorders in our community and has an incidence of between 1/1500 and 1/2500. The condition is characterised by chronic respiratory problems and even with today's treatment death in late childhood or early adult life is common. In addition to the respiratory disease patients show evidence of disturbed pancreatic function with steatorrhoea and failure to thrive. Some infants present with intestinal obstruction in the newborn period due to meconium ileus.

Fig. 5.6 demonstrates the mechanism of recessive inheritance. Both

* Adrenogenital Syndrome
* Agammaglobulinaemia (some types)
* Albinism (complete form)
  Alkaptonuria
  Ataxia - Telangiectasia
  Bloom Syndrome
  Conradis Disease
* Cystic Fibrosis
  Dandy - Walker Syndrome
* Deafness (some types)
  Epidermolysis Bullosa Dystrophica
  Galactosaemia
* Glycogen Storage Disease
  Hartnup Disease
  Histidinaemia
  Homocystinuria
  Hyperprolinaemia
  Ichthyosis (Collodion Fetus)
  Kallmann Syndrome
  Krabbe Leucodystrophy
  Laurence - Moon - Biedl Syndrome

* Letterer - Siwe Disease
  Lipidosis
  Lipodystrophy
  Maple Syrup Urine Disease
* Microcephaly (some types)
* Microphthalmus
* Mucopolysaccharidoses (some types)
  Pituitary Dwarfism
  Renal Tubular Acidosis
* Retinitis Pigmentosa
  Roberts Syndrome
  Russell - Silver Dwarfism
* Sickle cell disease
  Smith - Lemli - Opitz Syndrome
* Spastic Paraplegia
  Suxamethonium Deficiency
* Tay - Sachs Disease
  Thanatophoric Dwarfism
  Tyrosinaemia
* Werdnig - Hoffman Disease
  Xeroderma Pigmentosum

*more frequent occurrence

Table 5.2   Recessively inherited conditions.

parents carry the abnormal gene but appear physically normal. This does not mean that they may not harbour some evidence of the condition, but it may be a biochemical disturbance only. Until we know the nature of the basic biochemical defect we will be unable to demonstrate it in the parents. The classical clinical features of the disease are seen in those offspring who inherit both abnormal genes. Of the other possible outcomes to a pregnancy it can be seen in 2 out of 3 there is a risk of a child being a carrier like the parents. In only 1 out of 3 can the offspring be said to have a normal phenotype, i.e. to have no clinical evidence of the disease, and a normal genotype, i.e. did not inherit the abnormal gene. The risk of an affected offspring, therefore, is 25 per cent or 1 in 4 and the risk of having a child who is a 'carrier' like the parents is 2:3. Patients with cystic fibrosis do not normally reproduce but if we were to examine the pedigrees of families with other types of recessive disease we would see that affected persons normally do not have affected offspring.

As with dominantly inherited disease the action of the gene is not an all-or-none phenomenon. In recessive disease the heterozygote carrier, although physically normal, may well manifest some biochemical evidence of the condition. Tay-Sachs disease is a good example and this disorder is seen most frequently in the Ashkenazic

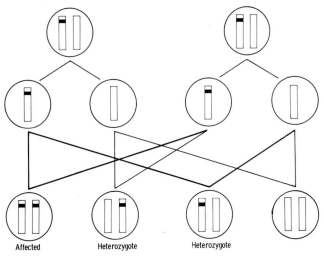

Fig. 5.6 Mechanism of recessive inheritance. Both parents, clinically normal, carry the abnormal gene and are heterozygotes. At reduction division the gene passes to half the sperm and half the ova. At fertilisation an individual with both genes will manifest the disease. This occurs in one of the four possible outcomes to fertilisation. Risk of child being heterozygous 2 : 3.

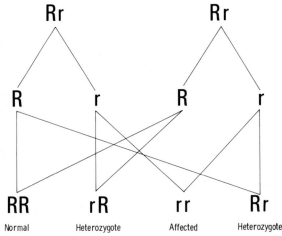

Fig. 5.7 Another method of demonstrating recessive inheritance. r is recessive to normal allele R. With a 'double dose' of r individual manifests disease.

Jewish population in North America. It causes mental retardation, blindness and a variety of neurological abnormalities all resulting from a deficiency of the enzyme hexosaminidase-A. Minor deficiencies of this enzyme can be detected in the heterozygotes who are clinically well. However, if they marry someone carrying the same recessive gene they have a 1 in 4 risk of producing an affected child. Since it is possible to detect individual carriers in a family it should be possible to screen large populations at special risk. Such a screening programme has been attempted in the American Ashkenazi Jews in selected areas with considerable success. Unfortunately, in most recessive diseases it is only possible to identify the asymptomatic carriers when they produce an affected child. In the majority there is no biochemical test which will clearly demonstrate the presence of the abnormal gene although hopefully with further research such tests will be available for some of the more common disorders.

Thalassaemia and sickle cell anaemia like Tay-Sachs Disease also produce manifestations in the 'carrier.' As they are very common conditions they should provide an opportunity for population screening and factual genetic counselling. Both are examples of a group of conditions called the haemoglobinopathies in which, as a consequence of an abnormal haemoglobin, there is an increased tendency to red cell breakdown and hence anaemia. In sickle cell disease it is possible to demonstrate an alteration in the haemoglobin molecule resulting from the gene mutation and this haemoglobin has a different amino-acid composition from normal haemoglobin. The difference between normal haemoglobin and that which produces sickle-cell anaemia is the result of an alteration in only one of the 146 amino-acids making up the haemoglobin molecule. This was one of the earliest demonstrations of the association between mutations in the genes and an alteration in chemical structure. In thalassaemia there is a block in the production of adult haemoglobin. This has been shown recently to result from loss of whole or part of the genes responsible for globin production. The mechanism is not yet clear but it is possible to demonstrate the trait in the carrier. The disease occurs mainly in people from the Mediterranean basin but in Great Britain is seen primarily in immigrants from India and Pakistan. There are several varieties of thalassaemia and patients who are homozygous for the abnormal gene suffer from anaemia and require frequent blood transfusions to survive. The heterozygote, with the abnormal gene and the normal allele, may have a less serious type of anaemia. This is referred to as thalassaemia minor as opposed to the major or more serious variety.

Obviously even a slight alteration of this nature may have serious consequences and this qualitative change is common in recessive disease. By changing the structure of the haemoglobin molecule red cells may assume abnormal shapes with consequent clinical effects.

The concept of a gene abnormality producing a single enzyme deficiency and hence a wide variety of clinical disease is now a well accepted one. It owes its origin to the work of Garrod who first described a condition called alkaptonuria. In this abnormality there is a deficiency of an enzyme which allows the urine to turn black on standing in air. There may also be an associated arthritis. Since Garrod's original work a large number of these so-called inborn errors of metabolism have been described and some occupy very famous places in the history of genetics. In phenylketonuria, as shown in Fig. 5.8, deficiency of an enzyme, phenylalanine hydroxylase, results in the various clinical manifestations. These include mental retardation often associated with microcephaly. Many of the patients have fair complexions with blue eyes and some also suffer from eczema. The disease is identified by demonstrating an abnormal excretion of phenylalanine in the urine. Other biochemical diseases may result from different enzyme deficiencies in the metabolic pathway of phenylalanine. Albinism results when there is a deficiency of melanin in the skin and this deficiency is produced by lack of an enzyme called tyrosinase. Alkaptonuria also results from disturbance of the metabolism of phenylalanine and the disease is due to a deficiency of the enzyme, homogentisic acid.

All of us carry a few abnormal genes but fortunately our spouse, also carrying some abnormal genes, usually carries different ones. However, the possibility of marrying someone carrying the same abnormal genes may be considerably increased by marrying a relative, particularly a first cousin. This is because first cousins share an eighth of their total genetic complement, their genome, with each other. With more distant relationships fewer genes are shared. This

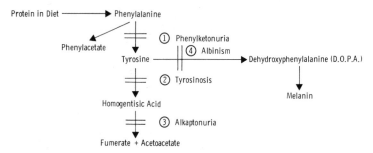

Fig. 5.8   Clinical conditions resulting from blocks at various stages in the metabolism of phenylalanine from diet.

basic inheritance pattern may explain some of the concern about first cousin marriages. Their only disadvantage may be the opportunity they afford for similar recessive genes to come together and hence produce disease. In some instances this may result in a biochemical deficiency causing mental retardation. In general there is not a high rate of first cousin marriages in either Great Britain or Europe but among some of our immigrant populations consanguinity is common and first cousin marriages are encouraged. This is demonstrated very clearly in Fig. 5.9, a pedigree of a Muslim family. It is obvious that there is a closer relationship than just first cousins and it should be equally obvious how much work is involved for the genetic nurse in compiling such a family pedigree.

The location or locus on the chromosomes of most genes responsible for common autosomal recessive disease is unknown. A probable exception is the gene responsible for a particular type of the adrenogenital syndrome; the variety associated with a deficiency of the enzyme, 21-hydroxylase. In this disease female infants may show marked enlargement of the clitoris and fusion of the labia. In addition they may have serious electrolyte disturbances with episodes of collapse which may end fatally. It has recently been demonstrated that the responsible gene lies close to the gene loci for an important system in the body called the HLA system. This system plays an

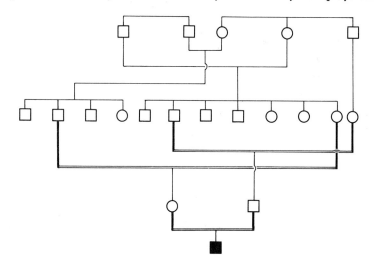

Fig. 5.9 Who is marrying who and who is related to who? Consanguinity: the marriage in generation III produced a male infant with bilateral severe microphthalmos. 1st cousin marriage is encouraged in some religious groups e.g. Muslims.

essential part in our immunological defence mechanism and the genes responsible are known to be on chromosome No. 6. They are situated on the smaller of the two arms of this chromosome and the various loci are designated A, B, C, D. The genes occupying these various sites are responsible for our specific tissue-type patterns and therefore, are of considerable importance in the expanding field of organ transplantation. For successful transplantation the tissues of the donor should match those of the recipient as far as possible; otherwise rejection may occur. The underlying principles are similar to those which have been studied in blood transfusion practice.

In addition this system is almost certainly involved in the body's response and immunity to disease. Recently it has been demonstrated that some chronic diseases such as ankylosing spondylitis are more likely to be associated with one particular tissue type – referred to as a *haplotype*, than another. How various tissue types produce susceptibility to certain chronic diseases is far from clear but a great deal of interest and research has been stimulated in this HLA system and human disease.

Summary of Characteristics of Recessive Inheritance
1. The disease characteristically appears only in sibs. The parents and other relatives are usually normal.
2. The risk of an affected person is 1 in 4 or 25 per cent.
3. In rare diseases it is more likely that the parents are consanguineous. In the more common conditions parents are usually unrelated.
4. Both sexes may be affected.

Agammaglobulinaemia (Bruton + Swiss Types)
° Albinism, Ocular
Aldrich Syndrome
Cleft Palate (some types)
° Colour Blindness
Diabetes Insipidus
Ectodermal Dysplasia
° Ehlers - Danlos Syndrome (type V)
Fabrys Disease
Glucose - 6 - Phosphate Dehydrogenase Deficiency (variants)
Glycogen Storage Disease (type VIII)
Gonadal Dysgenesis (Female Type)
° Haemophilia. A.
° Haemophilia. B. (Christmas Disease)

° Hydrocephalus (Aqueductal Stenosis)
Hypophosphataemic Rickets
Ichthyosis
Incontinentia Pigmenti
Menkes Syndrome
° Microphthalmia
Mucopolysaccharidosis (Hunter Type II)
° Muscular Dystrophy - Duchenne
Muscular Dystrophy - Becker
Spastic Paraplegia Syndrome
° Retinitis Pigmentosa
Telecanthus - Hypospadias Syndrome
° Testicular Feminisation
Wildervancks Syndrome

° more frequent occurrence

Table 5.3   Sex-linked disorders.

Sex-linked Diseases

When a disease results from the action of a gene carried on the sex chromosomes it is said to be sex-linked. As there appears to be no serious disability from the genes carried on the Y chromosome, sex-linked disease is commonly referred to as X-linked. In addition, although dominantly inherited X-linked disease does occur – a variety of vitamin D resistant rickets is transmitted in this fashion – the common X-linked diseases are recessively inherited. X-linked diseases are not as numerous as those due to other modes of inheritance, nevertheless, the 100 or more conditions so far described contain some common and serious childhood problems.

The pattern of inheritance can be seen in Fig. 5.10. In this situation the abnormal gene is carried on the X chromosome and the presence of the normal allele on the other X chromosome 'protects' the female from the disease. In the male, however, the abnormal gene on his X chromosome is not balanced by a normal allele on his small Y and he manifests the disease. Because the male can only have one of a pair of any X-linked genes he is said to be *hemizygous*. Of the possible outcomes to fertilisation it is apparent that any son born to a carrier female will have a 50 per cent chance of having the condition. Equally it is clear that any daughter has the same chance, 50 per cent,

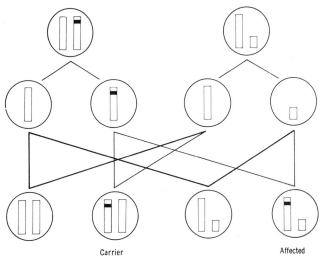

Carrier   Affected

Fig. 5.10   Recessively inherited X-linked disease. The abnormal gene is shown in one of the female X chromosomes. Each daughter with 2 X chromosomes has a 50/50 chance of inheriting the gene. Each son with no protecting normal allele has 50/50 chance of the disease.

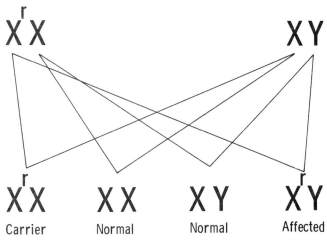

Fig. 5.11   Recessive gene r on X-chromosome produces disease
in the hemizygous male. 50/50 chance of carrier female.

of being a carrier like mother. Because it is the X chromosome which
carries the abnormal gene an affected male can never transfer the
disease to his sons but all his daughters will be carriers.

The pedigree in Fig. 5.12 is of a family in which several members
are affected by haemophilia. This disease results from a deficiency of
factor VIII, the antihaemophilic globulin. In generation II, two
males are affected and their mother must therefore be a carrier of the
disease. Her daughter must also be a carrier as she in turn produced
an affected son. In view of what we have learned of X-linked
recessive disease any daughter born to a carrier has a 50/50 risk of
being a carrier like her mother. One daughter has already had three
sons none of whom are affected and this clearly would suggest that
she might not be a carrier. The other daughter has only one unaffected male and this does not allow us to draw any conclusions
about her carrier status.

In X-linked disease it is obviously important to have some method
of detecting the carrier status of any female in the family. This may be
very apparent from the pedigree and if mother has an affected
brother and subsequently gives birth to an affected child then she
must be a carrier, a so-called obligatory carrier. Where a woman has
a single affected male child only, however, and no other family
history, then the son's disease could have arisen as a result of a
mutation in the gametes, i.e. ova or sperm, of either mother or father;
the same mechanism was discussed in dominantly inherited disease.
This is probably the situation in only about a third of all cases. In

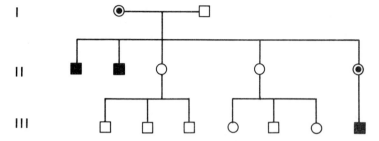

Fig. 5.12   A touch of class! Haemophilia affected the Royal heads of Europe until Queen Victoria's time. In this family grandmother in generation I had two affected sons, a carrier daughter, and an affected grandson.

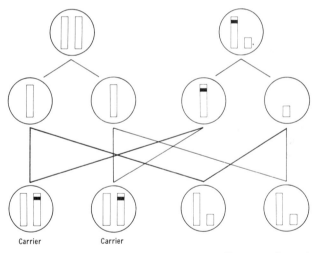

Carrier   Carrier

Fig. 5.13   X-linked recessive disease. An affected male with abnormal gene on his X chromosome produces carrier daughters, but never affected sons, to whom he must pass his normal Y chromosome.

haemophilia it is possible to detect the partial deficiency of factor VIII in a proportion of carrier females. This is very helpful information to obtain if a family requests genetic counselling. Unfortunately, only about 75 per cent of all heterozygotes (carriers) can be detected in this way and this still leaves 25 per cent or so who will have normal levels.

Summary of Characteristics of X-linked Recessive Inheritance
1. The trait is normally passed from a carrier female to her male offspring.
2. Sons have a 50/50 chance of inheriting the gene and therefore of developing the disease; daughters a 50/50 chance of being carriers like mother.
3. An affected male cannot pass the disease to his sons but all his daughters will be carriers. (This only applies to X-linked disease where an affected male survives into adulthood and is capable of reproduction. This is not the case with Duchenne muscular dystrophy which in genetic terms is said to be lethal and implies failure to reproduce.)
4. Daughters of affected males can pass the disease to their sons.
5. In some X-linked disease females may show some clinical evidence of the condition.

This last point would obviously be difficult to understand unless one remembers that a similar situation may occur in autosomal recessive inheritance. In this type of inheritance it is possible in some conditions, e.g. thalassaemia or Tay-Sachs Disease, to demonstrate that the carrier of the abnormal gene may have some evidence of the disease. The same principles apply to X-linked traits and the female carrier may manifest biochemical evidence of the disease without necessarily having any clinical signs of the disorder. This is explained

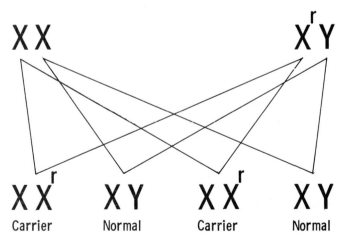

Fig. 5.14   The same again. X-linked recessive inheritance. The X chromosome from an affected male must produce carrier state in females.

by the behaviour of the X chromosomes in the normal female. Only one of the X chromosomes appears to be necessary for normal body function. The male after all has only one X chromosome and he manages without difficulty! The other female X chromosome therefore 'rests' normally and can be identified in body cells, e.g. in buccal mucosal cells as the chromatin mass or Barr body. The name is derived from the doctor who first described it and the chromatin mass lies at the periphery of the nucleus. It is seen in a higher percentage of cells in the female than in the male and females are usually reported as chromatin positive and males as chromatin negative. The inactivation of one of the X chromosomes occurs after there has been a period of cell division in the very early zygote. There will therefore be generations of cells with two active X chromosomes and these will continue to produce daughter cells. When inactivation occurs, however, one chromosome will form the resting Barr body and not influence cellular activity. It may be that this is the one containing the abnormal gene and there will, therefore, be only very minimal effects of the gene to be found. If, on the other hand, it is the active X chromosome which contains the abnormal gene then there is likely to be more evidence of the disease. This is called the Lyon hypothesis after Dr Mary Lyon who described it.

Conditions inherited in an X-linked dominant fashion are rare. Hypophosphataemic vitamin D resistant rickets and incontinentia

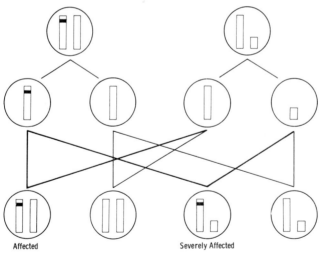

Affected   Severely Affected

Fig. 5.15 Sex linked dominant disease. An affected female produces severely affected males. There is no 'balancing' normal allele.

X - LINKED DOMINANT

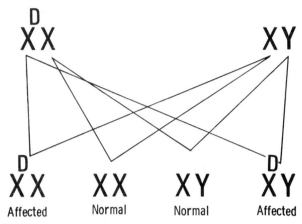

Fig. 5.16   In sex-linked dominant disease the male is at a disadvantage. With only one X chromosome he may not survive. The condition may therefore be less common in the male sex.

pigmenti are, however, seen on occasions. Incontinentia pigmenti is a serious skin disorder characterised by the gradual discolouration of scattered papular lesions on the trunk and face. In addition the patient may have mental retardation and heart disease. The transmission of these abnormalities is similar to autosomal dominant conditions in the female. If the dominant gene located on the X chromosome is responsible for serious disease the female with two X chromosomes and hence a normal allele may manifest the condition. The male, however, has no 'balancing' allele and may have a much more serious form of the disease. This may result in fetal or early neo-natal death of affected males so that this type of genetic disease will be more common in females. The other criteria for this form of inheritance are that each child, irrespective of sex, born to an affected female has a half risk of having the disease and affected males who survive transmit the trait to all their daughter but to none of their sons.

Chromosomal Abnormalities

Whereas genes cannot be visualised by any current means it is possible to detect alterations in the number and structure of chromosomes by examining a karyotype. It is only since 1956 that the correct number of chromosomes in man has been known but since that time there have been significant advances. The study of chromosomes and their abnormalities is referred to as *cytogenetics*. A karyotype may be prepared from peripheral blood obtained by venipuncture, from bone marrow or from skin cells. Lymphocytes in the peripheral blood are stimulated to divide by the addition of a substance called phytohaemagglutinin, a non-specific growth stimulator. At a certain stage in the culture of the cells, derivatives of the drug colchicine are added. This halts further division at a stage when the chromosomes have condensed, split into two chromatids and can be most easily identified. When saline is added to the preparation, the cells become swollen and the chromosomes more easily separated. They are then photographed under high magnification and arranged in pairs in descending order of size. There are 22 pairs of autosomes and a pair of sex chromosomes and these can be seen in Fig. 5.17. As a result of improvements in staining techniques it is now possible to identify more accurately each individual chromosome and this is now standard practice in most laboratories. For very accurate identification the light and dark areas in the individual chromosomes are assigned special numbers so it is possible to detect the loss or deletion of even a small portion of a chromosome.

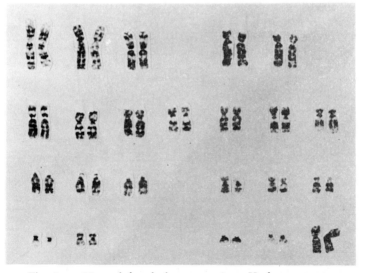

Fig. 5.17 Normal female karyotype (two X chromosomes, bottom right). Banded chromosomes. This staining technique is now routine in most laboratories. Karyotype shorthand 46,XX.

48   CLINICAL GENETICS

Autosomal Disorders		Incidence /1,000 births
Downs Syndrome	Trisomy 21	1.5
Pataus Syndrome	Trisomy 13	0.1
Edwards Syndrome	Trisomy 18	0.2
Cri – du – Chat Syndrome	Deletion 5	rare
Wolfs Syndrome	Deletion 4	rare

Sex Chromosome Disorders

Turners Syndrome	XO	0.4/1,000 females
Klinefelters Syndrome	XXY	1.2/1,000 males
Triple X – female	XXX	0.8/1,000 females
Double Y – male	XYY	1.0/1,000 males

Table 5.4 Chromosomal abnormalities with approximate
incidence.

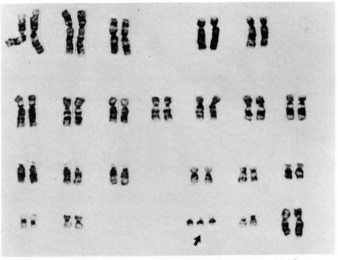

Fig. 5.18 Karyotype of female infant with Down's Syndrome
associated with trisomy 21 (Arrow). The bend in chromosome
No. 1 is an artefact produced during preparation. Karyotype
shorthand 47,XX,+21. More advanced techniques of chromosome identification suggest it may be No. 22 and not No. 21
which is involved.

There are 46 chromosomes in the nucleus of each body cell and
diseases associated with abnormalities of these chromosomes may be
the result of alterations in the total number, either too many or too
few, or from alterations in their structure. Structural changes may

result from the loss of a portion of a chromosome, a *deletion*, or from the interchange of chromosomal material from one chromosome to another, a so-called *translocation*. In this situation a portion of one chromosome breaks off and attaches itself to an adjacent chromosome.

The first and still one of the most common clinical syndromes associated with a demonstrable chromosomal anomaly is Down's Syndrome. This is characterised by mental retardation, an abnormal facies and an increased frequency of congenital heart disease. When we compare the karyotype of a child with this condition (Fig. 5.18) with that from a normal child it can be seen that group 21 consists of three instead of the usual two chromosomes. This is referred to as trisomy 21. For reasons which are not clear having an additional chromosome in this way has serious effects on the development of an individual. Presumably decoding the genetic information is disturbed but exactly in what way is unknown. Theoretically, it is possible to have trisomy of any of the autosomes but No. 21 appears to be particularly vulnerable and there is no satisfactory explanation for this phenomenon. Most chromosomal abnormalities of this type

Fig. 5.19   Down's Syndrome. This girl shows the typical round face, wide spacing of the eyes, epicanthal folds at the inner canthus, and upturned snub nose.

produce a combination of physical anomalies and varying degrees of mental retardation. Individuals affected in this way tend to grow poorly *in utero* and in general to have small birth weight. There is no single feature which can be said to be characteristic of a specific chromosomal abnormality and many of them have abnormal physical features in common. Nevertheless, specific clusters of physical abnormalities may combine to produce a characteristic clinical picture such as is seen in Down's Syndrome and some of the other classical chromosomal syndromes. Following the demonstration of trisomy 21 in children with Down's Syndrome there have been many other clinical syndromes identified with trisomy of other groups. As with other genetic disease there may be a variation in the clinical severity of these conditions. However, mental retardation is common to most of them and in some can be shown to be due to impaired brain cell growth.

Alterations of Chromosome Number (Aneuploidy)
Down's Syndrome has an incidence of 1.5/1000 births. It has recently been demonstrated as a result of the increased frequency of amniocentesis that the incidence at conception is higher. Some fetuses with this abnormality must therefore be rejected and lost early in pregnancy. This natural selective termination is obviously of great interest but so far the mechanism underlying it is completely unknown.

In addition to the physical characteristics mentioned it has been confirmed that in Down's Syndrome and most other clinical syndromes due to chromosomal abnormalities there are changes in the dermal ridge patterns of the hands and feet. The study of these abnormalities is called *dermatoglyphics*. The demonstration of such changes may be of help in diagnosis although rarely absolutely specific for a particular abnormality. Prints of the fingers, palms and the soles are normally obtained by pressing the hands or feet onto a pad containing a dye, and then onto special paper. A reasonable print can usually be obtained in this way but the technique takes some practice and the interpretation of the findings needs considerable expertise. There may be a single transverse palmar crease instead of the usual two. This is referred to as a Simian crease. In addition there may be a reduction in the number of dermal ridges on the fingers and toes. The science of dermatoglyphics has been established for many years and has been developed by police forces throughout the world. Apprehensive individuals should be told that they are not being fingerprinted in the usual way!

Trisomies of other autosomes, although less common, do result in a number of well recognised clinical syndromes and new ones are

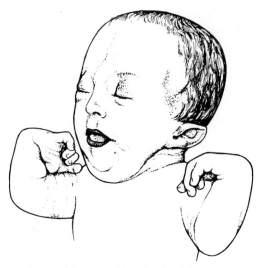

Fig. 5.20 Typical facies and hands of a child with trisomy 18. Poorly developed lower jaw, abnormal ears and a triangular face. The fingers are usually crossed and flexed.

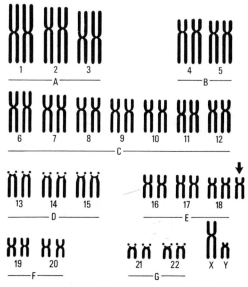

Fig. 5.21 Karyotype of child with trisomy 18. (Arrow) This is written 47,XY,+18.

being added regularly. It is a sensible precaution to examine the karyotype of any baby with an unexplained cluster of congenital abnormalities and particularly an infant who has an odd facial appearance and developmental delay. Individuals or children with such abnormalities are often said to be *dysmorphic* or to have dysmorphic features.

Fig. 5.20 shows the characteristic features of infants with trisomy 18. Some of these children do survive into later childhood and one such patient aged 12 has been found in a mental institution. They are invariably mentally retarded and many show flexion deformities of the wrists and crossed-over fingers. The facies is very striking and most have severe congenital heart disease. The very severe abnormalities associated with trisomy 13 (Fig. 5.22) could scarcely be missed but it is important to remember that some patients with these facial characteristics do not have a chromosomal abnormality. The clinical syndrome is collectively referred to as holoprosensephaly and consists of a grossly abnormal face and a poorly developed brain. Such abnormalities may be seen in other syndromes. The deep furrows in

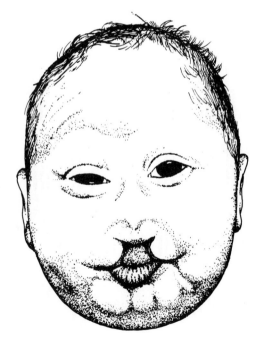

Fig. 5.22   Trisomy 13. An ugly deformity by any standards. Usually severely retarded and fortunately most die early in life.

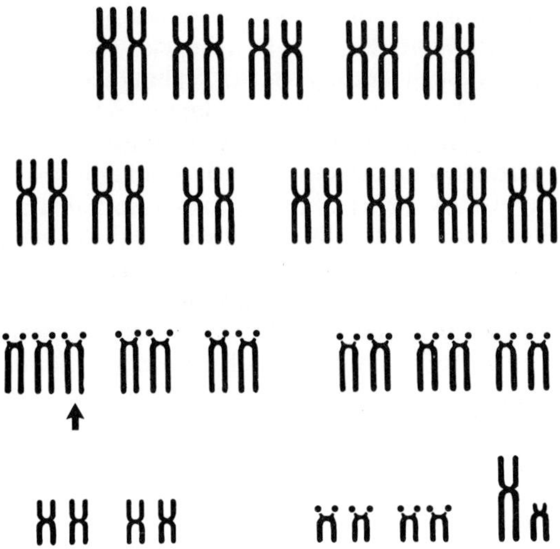

Fig. 5.23 Karyotype showing trisomy 13. Written 47,XY,+13.

Fig. 5.24a Trisomy 8. Face normal. Some patients have an abnormal round facies with deep set eyes.

the hands and feet causing thickened dermal pads appear to be characteristic of trisomy 8 (Fig 5.24a). As with other chromosomal anomalies there is usually mental retardation but the patients may have a fairly normal appearance. The wistful look is very characteristic.

It has been recognised for many years that the incidence of Down's Syndrome increases with maternal age. It is thought this is related to the increasing risk of abnormalities of chromosomal division during meiosis. When somatic cells divide to produce the gametes in either the male or female there should be an equal distribution of chromosomes to each daughter cell. The result should be that each of these cells contains half the total number of body chromosomes. This is what happens in normal meiosis. Subsequently at fertilisation the normal number, the so-called diploid number, is reconstituted. In some cases equal distribution of chromosomes to the daughter cells does not occur. In trisomy 21 both No. 21 chromosomes migrate to

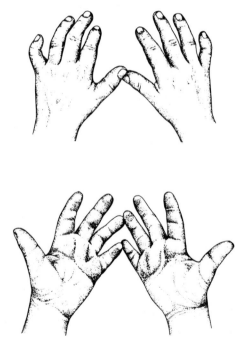

Fig. 5.24b   Trisomy 8. Intellectual retardation and abnormality of hands are main features. Incurved little fingers (clinodactyly), flexed fingers (camptodactyly), thick dermal pads on palms. Transverse palmar crease (simian crease) on left palm.

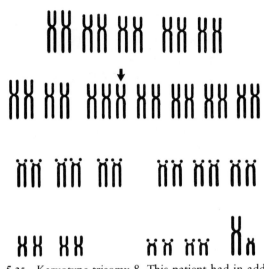

Fig. 5.25   Karyotype trisomy 8. This patient had in addition
some cells with a normal karyotype and was therefore said to be
a mosaic. His karyotype – 47,XY,+8/46,XY.

one daughter cell and none to the other daughter cell. This is seen in
Fig. 5.26 and is referred to as *non-disjunction*.

At fertilisation a sperm carrying a normal single No. 21 chromosome fertilises the ovum containing two No. 21s and trisomy ensues.
A similar mechanism underlies other trisomic abnormalities. There
is no clear explanation for the occurrence of non-disjunction. It is
seen in the male also but seems to happen more frequently in the
female, particularly in the animal kingdom. One explanation may be
that as the female ages her ovaries are increasingly subject to
environmental teratogens. She has all her ova from birth whereas the
male continues to make new generations of sperms throughout his
reproductive life, which can be very prolonged. Which environmental teratogens might be responsible for causing non-disjunction in
man is unknown. Irradiation, drugs or chemicals have not been
positively incriminated. In trisomy 21 there was a suggestion that the
non-disjunction might have resulted from damage caused by the
virus of hepatitis but this has not been definitely confirmed. In
animals there may be genes predisposing to non-disjunction but
these have not been demonstrated in the human. It is of interest,
however, that there have been many instances when a woman has
had a baby with one type of trisomy and subsequently has an infant
with a different trisomy. Despite the clear association with maternal
age it is a fact that the majority of babies with Down's Syndrome are

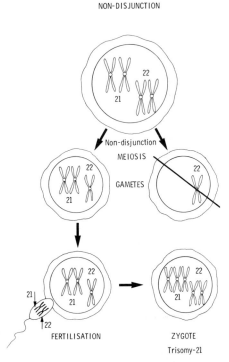

NON-DISJUNCTION

Fig. 5.26   Non-disjunction. Behaviour of chromosomes No. 21 and 22 at meiosis. The cell lacking chromosome No. 21 does not survive.

born to mothers of normal reproductive age. This is because fewer women over the age of 40 have babies and in the younger mothers it is still non-disjunction or similar cause of unequal chromosome distribution which is most likely to result in trisomy 21. Approximately 92 per cent of all children with this syndrome have this type of chromosomal abnormality. In the remainder some other chromosomal anomalies can be present but the end result is still the same and the babies have the usual features of Down's Syndrome.

More recently trisomies of portions of chromosomes, either the short or long arm, have been described and clinical syndromes are associated with their presence. Trisomy of the short arm of No. 9 chromosome is now well established and the clinical features show the usual combination of mental retardation and various physical anomalies. As with the full trisomic syndromes it is theoretically possible to have partial trisomy of any of the autosomes, either of the short arm or of the long arm.

Individual autosomes contain a large number of important and essential genes and loss of any one of the autosomes appears to be incompatible with survival. It is possible, however, to lose one X chromosome and survive. Such a situation results in an individual with the karyotype in Fig. 5.27. Here the problem is too few chromosomes and not too many as in the trisomies. This is usually written X0 and referred to as monosomy-X. The clinical features of the patient with this karyotype are well recognised. Female infants may present early in life with bilateral lymphoedema of the feet. Many show webbing of the neck and all are stunted in height. There is an increased risk of intellectual retardation and congenital heart disease. The diagnosis can obviously be confirmed by chromosomal analysis but it may also be suspected by examination of the buccal mucosal cells for the presence of a *Barr body*. As we have seen this chromatin mass is an inactivated condensed X chromosome. In Turner's Syndrome with only one X chromosome the patients are said to be chromatin negative like the male. In triple X females as would be expected with an extra X chromosome there are two Barr bodies to be seen in the buccal cells. Some of these patients have normal intelligence but a proportion are prone to psychiatric illness and mental subnormality. Physically they are usually normal.

As a result of more frequent cytological examination of abortuses and aborted material, the X0 constitution has been shown to be a

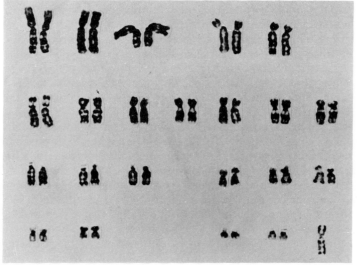

Fig. 5.27 Karyotype X0. It is possible to survive with just one X chromosome (bottom right).

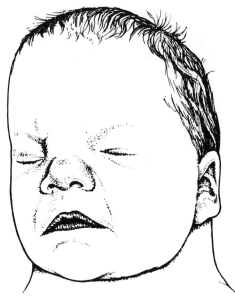

Fig. 5.28   Turner's Syndrome. The neck webbing and abnormal face is very obvious. Some girls have more normal appearance.

common finding. However, there is a substantial loss of fetuses with this abnormality so that at birth the incidence is 1 per 2500 newborn females. There is no obvious explanation for this occurrence. In some malformations the placenta is also abnormal and incapable of sustaining a pregnancy to term. However, this is not always the case and we do not know why some very grossly abnormal babies are retained in the uterus while others are rejected. Non-disjunction is the basis for the X0 constitution as well as for other numerical abnormalities. During meiosis the two X chromosomes may fail to disjoin or separate normally. The cell without the X chromosome, when fertilised by a sperm carrying an X chromosome, will have therefore only a single X constitution. Non-disjunction can also explain other abnormalities of the sex chromosomes. For example, the daughter cell with two X chromosomes, on fertilisation by an X-bearing sperm, will become a triple X cell. If it is fertilised by a Y-bearing sperm then Klinefelter's Syndrome, a male with two XX chromosomes, will result. Some children with all the features of Turner's Syndrome may be found to have two X chromosomes instead of just one. On closer inspection, however, one of the X chromosomes is seen to be larger than its fellow. This occurs as a

 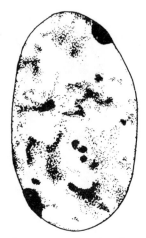

Fig. 5.29   The Barr Body in buccal mucosa cells. Another important difference between male and female. The single darkly-staining body is a resting chromosome from a female who is chromatin positive. Males are usually chromatin negative. The other cell shows two chromatin bodies. This is from a female with XXX constitution. The X0 female is chromatin negative.

result of abnormal division of the chromosome during cell division. The X chromosome divides transversely instead of longitudinally at the centromere. This results in a long and short chromosome instead of two identical halves. The short arm is lost and the long arm, called an isochromosome, survives. There has been sufficient genetic material lost in this process to produce the features of Turner's Syndrome.

Although the Y chromosome carries relatively little genetic information, in addition to the coded instruction necessary for 'maleness', it does have essential genes. In Klinefelter's Syndrome there are at least two X chromosomes in addition to the Y. This is a common sex chromosome abnormality with a frequency similar to trisomy 21. However, it is likely that some males with this condition go unrecognised. Many of them are picked up when they attend infertility clinics and others because of breast enlargement, gynaecomastia. In neither case may the affected person feel obliged to seek medical help.

There is some evidence that the other common abnormality, the XYY syndrome, is associated with an increased tendency to psychiatric problems and anti-social behaviour. However, other males with a similar chromosomal abnormality do not exhibit such characteristics and there is obviously a need for further information

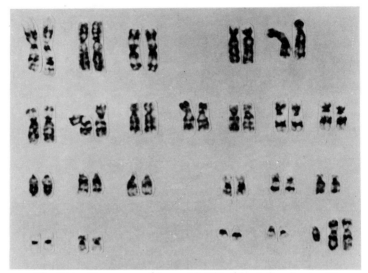

Fig. 5.30 Karyotype of boy with Klinefelter's Syndrome. 47, XXY. The two X chromosomes and the male Y chromosome are bottom right.

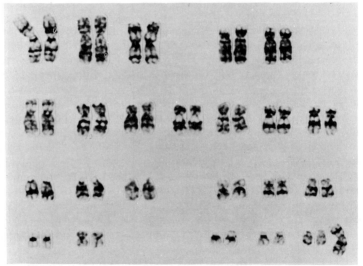

Fig. 5.31 Karyotype of boy with two Y chromosomes and one X chromosome. This young man looked angelic but attended the clinic with his probation officer. He had burned down his school and escaped to try again. Such antisocial behaviour is not a constant finding.

on this disorder. The patients look clinically normal and as a result of a recent television programme the public are already aware of the interest in the XYY male. He has been portrayed as having a superabundance of male characteristics, but this is not the case.

Structural Changes in Chromosomes

Common types of structural changes are *deletions* in which there is loss of a part of a chromosome and, therefore, loss of some genetic information. The missing portion may be at the end of a particular chromosome or it may be that breaks occur at both ends of the chromosome and the broken ends then unite to form a ring structure. Such a ring chromosome is generally unstable and during meiosis may not be transmitted intact. It may therefore produce abnormalities. A more common situation is when chromosome breakage occurs and the broken fragment of one chromosome attaches itself to another chromosome. This is referred to as a *translocation* and it may or may not produce clinical abnormalities. Provided there has been no significant loss of genetic material then the re-arrangement of chromosomes in this way may not have any ill effects. In this case the translocation is said to be balanced. However, such translocations may interfere with normal meiosis and the formation of gametes, so that the resultant new individual may have either too much chromosomal material or too little. In either case clinical abnormalities may result and the translocation is then considered to be unbalanced.

Translocation   Such a structural re-arrangement is important in some cases of Down's Syndrome and the karyotype in Fig. 5.32a is of a child with a translocation. The karyotype of the carrier mother is also shown. No other members of the family were affected. In this situation mother has not lost any significant amount of genetic material even though she has only 45 chromosomes. Her No. 21 is in fact transposed or translocated onto the top of chromosome No. 14. However, during the production of her gametes some ova will be abnormal and carry the extra No. 21 chromosome. At fertilisation with the normal sperm carrying one No. 21 an individual is formed with three No. 21s. This is essentially trisomy 21 despite the fact that the extra No. 21 chromosome is attached to chromosome No. 14.

It is important when a translocation is found in a family that all sibs and the relatives of the carrier parent are examined. By this means it may be possible to detect those with a balanced translocation and therefore at risk of having an abnormal child. They should be given adequate genetic counselling and would normally be offered amniocentesis during pregnancy. Translocations involving the chromosome No. 21 and chromosomes in the group 13–15 seem to

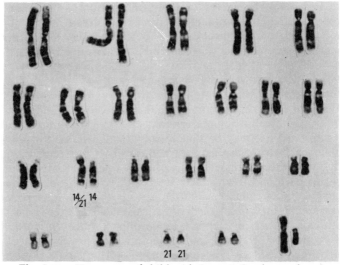

Fig. 5.32a Karyotype of child with Down's Syndrome due to an unbalanced translocation – an extra chromosome, No. 21 is translocated onto chromosome No. 14. This abnormality has been inherited from mother. Total chromosome No. is 46, but one of these is the abnormal translocation chromosome.

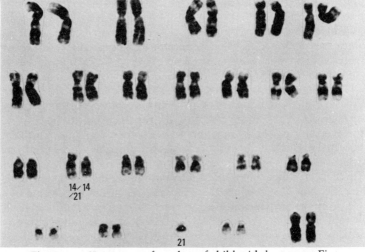

Fig. 5.32b Karyotype of mother of child with karyotype Fig. 5.32a. This woman has only two chromosomes No. 21. One is attached to chromosome No. 14, as in her child. The total chromosome No. is only 45 but the lost No. 21 is on No. 14.

be more common than translocations of the G group with other autosomes. However, translocations between other chromosomes may be found in situations in which it may be very difficult to define their exact role. For example, balanced translocations are found in about 10 per cent of women who have frequent miscarriages or failed pregnancies and also in a number of men who have infertility. An unusual situation is seen in Fig. 5.33. The woman or man with the translocation may have no other physical abnormality. It is difficult to explain how the translocation apparently 'balanced' in most other respects could selectively interfere with reproductive abilities. Should a person carrying a balanced translocation become pregnant it is import-ant that her attendants are made aware of her risk of having a child with an unbalanced form of the abnormality. Unbalanced trans-locations irrespective of the particular chromosomes involved are frequently associated with severe physical and mental abnormalities.

It is probable that a number of chromosomal abnormalities go unrecognised in medical practice. Although it has been suggested that chromosomal abnormalities account for only about 1 per cent of all disease in childhood this figure is undoubtedly a low estimate.

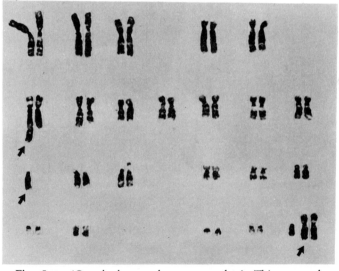

Fig. 5.33 'One bad turn deserves another'. This unusual karyotype was found in a male with infertility. He has Klinefel-ter's Syndrome with two X chromosomes. In addition he has a balanced translocation and chromosome No. 13 is translocated onto the end of chromosome No. 6. Because he has Klinefelter's Syndrome and is infertile he cannot pass on his translocation.

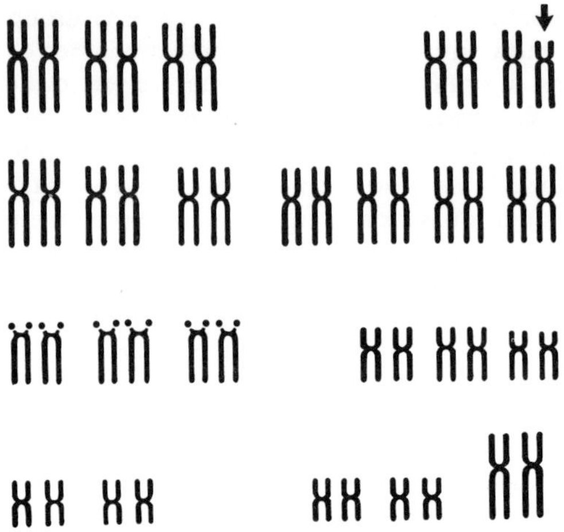

Fig. 5.34 Deletion of short arm of chromosome No. 5. Although only a small piece of chromosome has been lost the effects are very serious. This karyotype is written 46,XX,5p–.

Fig. 5.35 Girl with the Cri-du-chat Syndrome. Her cry was abnormal when she was a baby but later became normal. She was mentally retarded and had a round face with wide-spaced eyes and a down-turned mouth.

A recent report suggests about 7 per cent of all children dying in the perinatal period and in the first year of life have a chromosomal abnormality. It is also recognised that in about 25–30 per cent of pregnancies which terminate in the first trimester there is a demonstrable chromosomal anomaly in the fetus.

Deletions   Fig. 5.34 shows loss of a portion of chromosome No. 5. That section of the chromosome above the centromere or junction point is referred to as 'p' and the longer section below the centromere is referred to as 'q'. The clinical syndrome associated with loss of a portion of 'p', although rare, is a very striking one and such children have a peculiar cry thought by some to resemble the miaowing of a cat. This is noted early in life and due to a softening of the larynx (laryngomalacia). It does not persist but the children remain mentally retarded and have associated physical abnormalities such as hypertonicity and a peculiar facies.

Deletion of the part of the short arm of chromosome No. 4 is a more recently described abnormality. There is normally no change in the cry and the clinical abnormalities are significantly different from those in the previous deletion. There is an abnormal facies, intellectual impairment and hypotonicity. Some children have hypospadias and seizures.

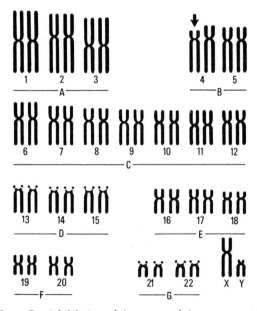

Fig. 5.36   Partial deletion of short arm of chromosome No. 4.
46,XY,4p −.

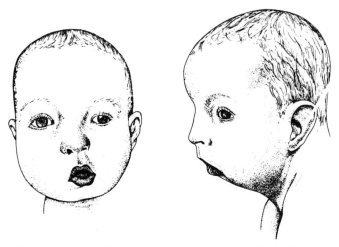

Fig. 5.37 Boy with facial asymmetry, micrognathia and mental retardation due to deletion of short arm of chromosome No. 4.

Polygenic or Multifactorial Inheritance

The diseases so far discussed have been considered to result from the action of a single gene or from abnormalities of the number or structure of chromosomes. Although the environment may have a modifying influence on the end product, in these situations it is essentially gene action which is the important element. There are many common disorders, however, in which although there is a genetic component, the inheritance pattern cannot be explained simply in terms of dominant or recessive traits and there are no demonstrable chromosomal changes. Instead it appears that it is the cumulative action of a number of genes which is important and it is this factor, a multiple gene or polygenic effect, which is responsible for the familial tendency or predisposition to these abnormalities. Individuals possessing such a genetic make-up and subject to the appropriate environmental stimulus or teratogen will develop evidence of the disease. Since this results from a combination of genetic and environmental factors it is referred to as multifactorial. In these conditions the severity of the disease may show considerable variation but exactly how the two major components interact is far from clear. Although the concept of multifactorial disease is a useful one and allows us to advise our patients, further advances in our understanding of gene action may provide a different explanation. Table 5.5 lists the common multifactorial diseases. Fig. 5.38 demonstrates how the combination of genetic and environmental factors may act to produce disease in the way that has been discussed. It suggests that there are some families with a genetic predisposition to a particular disease who, with the appropriate environmental stimulus, may be pushed over the threshold and hence develop the disease. Such a model can also be used to show that first degree relatives are at

Anencephaly
Congenital Dislocation Hip
Congenital Heart Disease
Congenital Pyloric Stenosis
Diabetes – some types
Hare Lip ± Cleft Palate
Spina Bifida
Spina Bifida + Meningomyelocele
Manic Depressive Psychosis
Schizophrenia
Talipes Equinovarus

Table 5.5   Multifactorial conditions.

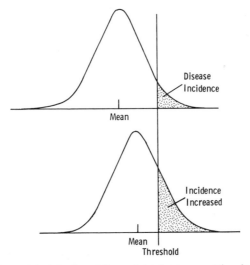

Fig. 5.38   Model of multifactorial inheritance. The distribution of liability or susceptibility to a multifactorial disorder in the general population is illustrated by the bell shaped curve in the top figure. In the lower figure the liability to the disease is shifted to the right i.e. the genetic contribution is increased and this results in an increased familial incidence of the condition.

greater risk than the general population. This is because the genetic effect would obviously be greater in close relatives sharing common genes and the effect would lessen with more distant relatives. Unfortunately, it is impossible in most cases to know whether the familial or environmental factors are playing the more important role.

As can be seen from the list many common conditions are included in this group. Most practising nurses and doctors will have experience of families in which certain diseases appear more commonly than in other members of the community. Whereas in single gene disorders the recurrence risk is high and remains unaltered for successive pregnancies, in multifactorial disease the recurrence risk after an affected child is low, usually less than 1/20. When there have been two affected children, however, the risk increases considerably to about 1 in 8 to 1 in 10. It might be as high as 1 in 4 after three affected children. Relatives of individuals who have had affected children have a definite but small increased risk of the same condition in their children.

The neural tube defects are the most common of the serious congenital abnormalities and many features of this disorder can be explained on a multifactorial basis. Thus the risk of any mother in our population having a baby with this condition is about 1 in 200. Following the birth of an affected child the risk for subsequent pregnancies is about 1 in 20. Should she be unlucky enough to have a second affected child then the risk for subsequent pregnancies rises to approximately 1 in 8. With three affected children the risk rises even higher, probably 1/4. Families with such a history were encountered before it was possible to diagnose the condition early in pregnancy.

This common abnormality is interesting from other aspects and demonstrates many of the features of combined genetic and environmental inheritance. For example, in Belfast the incidence is 7/1000 and in South Wales even higher whereas in East Anglia and South-East England it is only about 2/1000. The increased tendency of those of Celtic stock to have affected children persists even in those Celts who go to live in North-Eastern America. This would obviously suggest a genetic contribution. It is also well recognised that neural tube abnormalities have a definite seasonal incidence, being commoner in winter months. Lower social classes are more often affected and the disease is more likely to affect the first and fourth children in a family. These various elements may be related to environmental factors.

However, such factors are present in very many other non-genetic conditions and there is a need to continue the search for other aetiological agents. Recently it has been suggested that a preceding

abortion or failed pregnancy might act as the stimulus for the production of some form of 'antibody'. This could then damage the
developing neural tube in a subsequent pregnancy. This exciting
suggestion obviously needs further investigation and highlights the
need for continuing research.

Fig. 5.39 is the pedigree of a family in which the first child was born
with a severe meningomyelocele and hydrocephalus. A second infant
died at the age of three months from meningitis. In her third pregnancy mother was found to have a raised serum alpha-fetoprotein
level. In view of her previous obstetric history it had already been
suggested that she should have amniocentesis and the liquor alphafetoprotein was also raised. Following discussion the parents
decided to terminate the pregnancy and a stillborn infant of 21 weeks
gestation was delivered and found to have a large meningomyelocele. Some months later the parents decided on a further
pregnancy. On this occasion both the serum and liquor alpha-
fetoproteins were normal and the mother was eventually delivered of a
healthy girl who showed no evidence of a congenital disorder. As can
be seen in the family pedigree a cousin of mother's had a child with
isolated hydrocephalus. This abnormality is most commonly seen in
association with spina bifida and meningomyelocele. In some cases it
occurs without a spinal lesion but is still considered to be part of the
neural tube abnormalities. In other patients the aetiology is entirely
different.

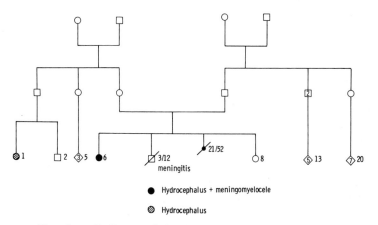

Fig. 5.39 Pedigree of family in which child III·6 has
hydrocephalus and meningomyelocele. A pregnancy was
terminated because of neural tube abnormality in the fetus. A
maternal cousin had isolated hydrocephalus.

	After 1st affected child	After 2nd affected child
Ventricular Septal Defect	1/25	> 1/10
Patent Ductus Arteriosus	1/30	1/10
Atrial Septal Defect	1/30	1/10
Tetralogy of Fallot	1/35	1/10
Pulmonary Stenosis	1/30	> 1/10
Aortic Stenosis	1/30	> 1/10
Transposition of Gt. Vessels	1/50	1/15
Endocardial Fibroelastosis	1/6	1/4

Table 5.6 Recurrence risk, congenital heart defects.

Fig. 5.40 Girl with the Ellis-van-Crevald Syndrome. Her short stature is primarily due to shortening of distal rather than proximal part of limbs. She has dentures and abnormalities of her hands.

It is important to remember that many conditions listed in this group may occur as part of a syndrome with an entirely different mode of inheritance. For example, if congenital heart disease occurs without associated abnormalities, then it may be of multifactorial origin. However, it may be found in about 25 per cent of children with Down's Syndrome and is often present in other chromosomal abnormalities such as Turner's Syndrome. On occasions it may also be associated with dominantly inherited diseases such as Marfan's Syndrome or with recessive conditions such as the Ellis-Van-Crevald Syndrome. Patients with this abnormality have short stature, abnormalities of the fingers and a widespread chondrodystrophy. They may also have an abnormal heart and an intellectual retardation.

If any of the conditions listed in the multifactorial group are part of a syndrome with a single gene pattern of inheritance, then the recurrence risk is appropriate to that of the syndrome. Meckel's Syndrome is a good example of this principle. In this condition the patient has an encephalocele associated with abnormalities of the kidneys and polydactyly. Encephalocele may occur as part of the spectrum of the neural tube anomalies and the recurrence risk is low. However, as part of Meckel's Syndrome it has a high recurrence risk as this syndrome is recessively inherited.

6

Genetic
Counselling

It is difficult to find a simple definition of genetic counselling which will satisfactorily explain its varying roles in different situations. In many cases it can be considered to be another aspect of clinical medicine advising about the recurrence risk of a particular abnormality; for example, estimating the risk of a further affected child following the birth of a child with Down's Syndrome or spina bifida. In other families it may be to advise about the possible occurrence of a specific disease. A good example is Huntington's Chorea and the son or daughter of affected parents may wish to know the chance of developing this disease.

As with other types of medical problems an accurate diagnosis is essential and adequate pedigree information necessary to decide on the mode of inheritance. In addition the nurse and doctor in the genetic clinic have to be very aware of the possible psychological factors associated with many family problems. They must also cultivate the ability to communicate facts sympathetically and in a way which is understood.

Another important role of the genetic counsellor is to alert the profession to the possibility of an infant being born with a congenital disorder. For example, a young couple who have had a child with the adrenogenital syndrome have a 1 in 4 chance of having a similarly affected infant. By alerting the medical attendants, any subsequent children can be tested for the condition soon after delivery and if shown to be affected they can be commenced on treatment. This preventative role is even more clearly demonstrated in the rapidly developing field of prenatal diagnosis. The association of genetic counselling services with obstetric management is already helping to reduce the incidence of some serious congenital anomalies in our community. On many occasions the genetic counsellor will be expected to play the role of diagnostician. It is not unusual for patients with rare diseases or clusters of physical abnormalities to be referred for an opinion and frequently for the exclusion of a chromosomal abnormality. This is an important aspect of the work and in most cases a reliable recurrence risk can only be given if a condition has been correctly diagnosed. Finally, some couples are referred because of concern about consanguinity or first cousin marriages. This is a common and accepted practice in some of our immigrant families but is still a cause of concern in most European cultures.

In virtually every case it is important to have a firm diagnosis, adequate details of the family pedigree and time for discussion. The aim is to ensure that all consultands are in a position to make informed and balanced judgements about their future. Although this is not always possible it is worth striving for. At all stages it is important to ensure that families who have been counselled have adequate support. In some individuals, emotional upset and anxiety may be aggravated or, more rarely, precipitated by the information they are given. The nursing staff and medical staff in the genetic service must be sensitive to this possibility and may have to enlist help from the general practitioner or other specialists. Many couples attending the clinic may decide not to have further children as a result of the information given to them. It is then the responsibility of the genetic nurse or doctor to ensure that they are referred to the appropriate area for advice on contraception. Some families may request specific advice on sterilisation or adoption and the nurse should be familiar with the referral procedures to the appropriate agencies. In dominantly inherited disease affecting the male member of a family, artificial insemination may be requested and details of this technique should be available.

The conditions listed in Table 6.1 show the type of referrals and this mixture of problems will be very similar to those seen in other areas. Enquiries by telephone and letter are common and although in many instances it is possible to answer these, it is usually safer to see the person concerned in the clinic.

Most genetic counselling services are associated with teaching hospitals or universities and there are approximately 30 throughout Great Britain. The siting of the clinic is important and it is unsatisfactory for a couple who have just lost a baby to have to visit a counselling service in a maternity hospital or busy paediatric outpatient department. A non-clinical environment is more appropriate and the atmosphere should be congenial and pleasant.

The staffing of individual counselling services varies and the involvement of nurses depends on a number of factors including the location of the clinic and the workload. Most services find the help of some type of nurse invaluable. The professional training and post-

Total Number 1973-1978	833
Miscellaneous Conditions	267
Single Gene Disorders	265
Multifactorial Conditions	189
Chromosomal Abnormalities	112

Single Gene Disorders		Miscellaneous Conditions	
Dominant	116	Intestinal Anomalies	61
Recessive	88	Oesphageal Atresia	
X - Linked	61	Exomphalos	
		Gastroschisis	
Chromosome Disorders		Ano - Rectal Abnormalities	
Autosomal Downs	70	Mental Retardation (non - specific)	41
Others	29	Mental Retardation (c̄ associated	
Sex Chromosome	13	abnormalities)	16
		Multiple Congenital Abnormalities	19
Multifactorial Conditions		Suspected Chromosomal Anomaly	28
Neural Tube Defects	144	Epilepsy (non - specific)	19
Congenital Heart Disease	33	Stillbirths	11
Hare Lip / Cleft Palate	9	1st Cousin Marriage	12
Talipes	2	Infertility	7
Diabetes	1	Recurrent Miscarriage	6
		Retinoblastoma (unilateral)	2
		Others	45

Table 6.1   Referrals to genetic counselling clinic.

graduate experience of the health visitor and paediatric nurse make them particularly suitable. Both should be aware of the familial consequences of disease and the paediatric nurse will have experience of the various problems resulting from congenital abnormalities. The health visitor can act as a link with the community services and will be familiar with many of the local problems. Since genetic counselling is a relative newcomer to medical practice there is still only a small number of nursing staff involved in this type of work. However, because of the increasing demand for the service it may be necessary to set up peripheral clinics and this will almost certainly mean more nursing involvement in the future.

The genetic nurse normally has responsibility for the organisation of the outpatient clinics. In conjunction with the secretary she arranges clinic lists, decides on the urgency of appointments and generally assures smooth running of all aspects of the service. Her knowledge of hospital routines including hospital record systems is valuable in the collection of patient information. With experience she can be responsible for the initial interview with the counsellees and may play a very important role in the assessment of individual family problems. In selected cases she may already have had contact with the parents, for example in the neo-natal unit or paediatric ward. In some circumstances she may have commenced the collection of pedigree information and helped some couples to overcome their natural anxiety about attending the clinic. The nurse must be familiar with the emotional problems facing many of the consultands and other family members. If she is the first person they meet at the clinic then she has a very important role in setting the tone for subsequent discussions and attendances.

The genetic nurse should be available to give emotional support to the couples attending for advice. She is present during the counselling session and will attempt to assess unasked questions. At the conclusion of the interview she may arrange for a home visit to answer questions which may not have been raised during the clinic session. She is also available to discuss other problems such as family planning, sterilisation or artificial insemination and can explain how detailed information on these services can be obtained. The health visitor attached to the service, because of her access to and acceptance by the community, is able to visit families at home, to obtain pedigree information and to enquire about failed attendances. Both the full-time genetics nurse and health visitor provide a very useful liaison role with their nursing colleagues, with family practitioners and with other medical personnel. In addition to these more traditional roles they are also responsible for assisting in the evaluation of the work of the clinic, a continuing activity which makes it necessary to interview all individuals who have been counselled. They also take part in regular clinical meetings with other staff members and are normally involved in research within the department. Because genetic counselling is still relatively new there is a great deal of observer interest. Many groups of nursing staff, medical students and other personnel may wish to attend the clinics. It is important that their visits are properly organised as too many observers may discourage frank discussion. This is another task normally delegated to the genetic nurse.

Many clinics employ social workers in addition to, or on occasions as an alternative to, nursing staff. Their training and experience usually makes them very useful members of the team. Other professional staff including psychologists may also be involved in specific aspects of the work. In some countries, particularly in the USA, genetic counselling may be performed by non-medical staff who have been trained in counselling techniques at various designated colleges. They normally graduate with a PhD in genetics and work in conjunction with medical and nursing staff.

Successful genetic counselling relies heavily on clinical expertise and sensitivity to patient problems. In their normal clinical practice, paediatricians and obstetricians are in frequent contact with patients suffering from congenital and genetic disorders and because of their involvement with such families should have developed skills appropriate to genetic counselling work. However, they must in addition have knowledge of clinical genetics and basic genetic principles. Very often the genetic counselling service is part of a department of medical genetics and the counselling advice may be offered by a medical geneticist as opposed to a doctor with a more clinical background. There is now a recognised specialist training programme for Clinical Geneticists and it is likely this will encourage more doctors to enter this field in future.

Experience from paediatric and obstetric services confirms that it is difficult and almost certainly inadequate to attempt to give genetic counselling in the normal busy out-patient clinics. Obviously it is possible to quote a recurrence risk as a brief statement of fact but if families with genetic problems are to be managed properly, time must be allowed for discussion and for further questions if necessary. The transition from the standard clinical doctor role to that of genetic counsellor cannot be made satisfactorily in a normal clinic setting and the opportunity afforded for health education may be lost. In those families in which high risk serious genetic disease is present, time to discuss all the possible implications is essential and these families, forming the central core of the counselling work, must be supported. This means that the number of referrals must be kept low and although this will vary, a minimum of an hour is probably necessary for a new referral and half this time for a repeat attendance.

Patients are normally referred from family doctors, hospital consultants and community physicians. Self-referrals are not generally accepted and such individuals or couples are best referred to their family doctor who will then normally agree to their attendance at the clinic. On occasions, the community nurse or health visitor may see the need for genetic counselling where the doctor concerned may not. This problem occurs in many aspects of medicine and it is still advisable for individuals to attend the clinic only with the agreement of their family doctor. He will, after all, have to be responsible for their continuing care.

Experience has shown that it is helpful to send appointees a short letter of explanation about the work of the counselling service prior to their first attendance. This briefly details the type of help given, the time normally needed for the interview and the importance of obtaining as much family pedigree information as possible prior to their first visit. Such a letter should be couched in friendly terms and

General Practitioner	313
Paediatrician	244
Obstetrician	134
Paediatric Surgeon	61
Community Paediatric Service	28
Orthopaedic Surgeon	10
Self Referral	8
Consultant in Mental Handicap	7
Neurologist / Neurosurgeon	12
Other Specialists	16
Total	833

Table 6.2   Referral source. Referrals from some specialities
still low. All referrals increasing annually.

it is important to remember that the impression conveyed by this
letter may well set the tone for subsequent interviews *(Appendix A)*.
It is helpful when making an appointment to suggest whether or not
it is necessary to bring children to the clinic. Where this is not essential,
parents may need help in arranging supervision of the children.

The timing of some referrals is very important. For example, in
families in which there has been the birth of a child with severe
congenital abnormalities the parents have a predictable emotional
reaction with varying degrees of depression, self-recrimination,
anger and even rejection of the infant. The duration of this reaction
varies considerably and some aspects of it may persist for months or
even years. In general, it is at least three months before the parents
are sufficiently emotionally stable to accept, understand and benefit
from the advice given. Niceties of recurrence risks may mean very
little to a woman still suffering from marked feelings of infant
rejection and depression. Awareness of these phenomena and proper
timing of referral need to be constantly stressed in discussion and
lectures to family doctors and hospital colleagues. In other couples,
motivation to attend the clinic may fall off considerably and the
waiting time should probably not exceed three months. This is seen
particularly in families where the referral has been prompted by the
general practitioner. Some members of these families may have failed
to grasp the importance of the problems or to appreciate the need to
attend. There is still need for further information on these various
aspects of clinic attendance.

Most consultands appear to benefit from more than one interview.
This is particularly the case in conditions associated with a high risk
of recurrence which may have considerable emotional impact. Re-
attendance affords the opportunity for further discussion and

assessment of the consultand's grasp of the facts. In some circumstances home visiting by the health visitor may be very helpful and discussion 'over a cup of tea' may be more beneficial than formal attendance at the counselling clinic. In many cases the genetic nurse may conduct the second and subsequent interviews and many couples find this more helpful than 'seeing the doctor'.

It is important that the consultands understand the information given and this may present problems and will certainly demand time. It is unrealistic to expect some people to grasp even simple concepts of probability and in some cases even simple biological facts. However, since the information given may have very serious consequences it is important that attempts are made to try and ensure some basic understanding of the situation. This inevitably means spending time and allowing the consultands the opportunity to ask questions. They should be sympathetically encouraged to talk about their views of the risk quoted and about their attitudes to childbearing and contraception. All of these factors will have an important bearing on their ultimate decision. Counselling normally implies a dialogue as opposed to the usual situation in a medical clinic where discussion may not be encouraged. In some centres consultands may be given additional written information and reports suggest that this is normally very helpful. It can be a very useful means of reinforcing the advice given at the clinic and families often retain the information for many years. Such a letter may attain the status of a family heirloom! *(Appendix B)*.

In many cases, particularly where there has been the birth of an abnormal baby, an excellent opportunity is provided for health education. This is an important aspect of genetic counselling work and would not be possible if time was always at a premium. Many referred families have misconceptions about the cause of their trouble and many women have strange ideas on the origin of congenital abnormalities. In most situations of this type the counsellor is in a position not only to discuss the basic questions of recurrence risks but also to help in the understanding of the problem. The discussion therefore frequently enables some of the consultands to gain more understanding of simple biological facts. This may also help them to gain insight into their relationship with one another and with their family.

In the earlier days of genetic counselling many referred couples tended to be highly motivated, middle-class and educated. With the service now available to a wider cross-section of the population many of the consultands come ill-prepared for any general discussion and are more concerned about the doctor advising them what to do about their problem. This changing demand on the counsellor needs further evaluation. Visual aids, simple explanatory booklets and other educational help can be employed for some people. However, many consultands may find discussion of chromosomes or genes too difficult.

These various facets of genetic counselling emphasise the importance of the counsellor, both doctor and nurse, becoming familiar with the techniques of education. There would seem to be good grounds therefore for genetic counselling clinics having close links with departments of health education.

As with other clinical problems it is important to keep proper notes and particular stress is laid on family pedigree information. Most hospital records do not contain sufficient information of this sort and in some there may be none at all. However, the increasing interest in clinical genetics may emphasise the need for general nursing and medical staff to pay more attention to pedigree details in future.

Concern has been expressed about the need for confidentiality of genetic information. This is certainly very important as it is with all medical information and means of ensuring confidentiality need to be considered. Most hospital record storage systems provide inadequate obstacles to a determined invader and most casenotes are readily accessible to a wide variety of hospital personnel. Computer registration of genetic information may provide one solution to this problem and it is possible to design a system which is reasonably secure. Several workers have shown considerable ingenuity in trying to ensure that their computer stored information is 'burglar-proof'. Despite the concentration of information stored it would require considerable expertise on the part of the invader to obtain it. In addition this method of information storage has the advantage of providing a rapid retrieval system and may be used as an aid to the ascertainment of genetic disease in the community. In most genetic services case notes are stored in the department and are not filed in the common hospital record department.

We have reviewed some of the factors in single gene, chromosomal and multifactorial disease and in reviewing the basic principles of meiosis we have laid the ground work for an understanding of how risks are calculated. We must now look at specific examples of referrals to the genetic clinic chosen to illustrate the various modes of inheritance and their management.

Single Gene Abnormalities

Dominant Inheritance
Fig. 6.1 is the pedigree of a family referred because Mrs M.'s first born male child was thought to suffer from tuberous sclerosis, or

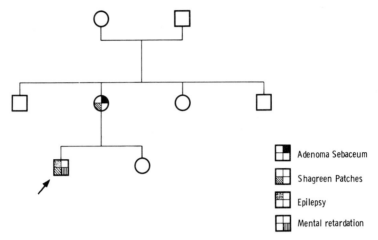

Adenoma Sebaceum

Shagreen Patches

Epilepsy

Mental retardation

Fig. 6.1   Tuberous sclerosis. The propositus marked with an arrow was mentally retarded and had other features as shown.

adenoma sebaceum. She had one other normal child. The family doctor's letter stated that mother had been extremely upset because of the delay in making the diagnosis and during the period of uncertainty about the child's future she became depressed and anxious. The practitioner had attempted to reassure her but in his letter mentioned that he had not seen such a condition before. When his request for an appointment arrived a letter was sent to Mrs M. detailing the work of the service. She was asked to give details of previous hospital attendances and the relevant notes were obtained. When she arrived at the clinic she was met by the genetic nurse and during the initial interview an assessment was made of her emotional state and the type of help she was seeking. Some attempt was also made to assess the impact of the disease on her family, her social life and her married life.

The family pedigree information obtained was brief. Her sister did not have any children but had heard about the diagnosis and was apparently very anxious to be seen at the clinic as she was hoping to marry fairly soon. Mrs M.'s mother and father were both alive and well. Neither had any stigmata of the disease. Her two brothers were also normal. It was established that Mrs M. had been to a secondary modern school and had coped there with difficulty. Her general health had been good and she did not suffer from convulsions. She had always had a facial rash which she developed early in life and which she accepted as acne. Her husband was in good health as were his parents, sibs and second degree relatives. During the initial interview Mrs M. was obviously very anxious and the suggestion that there was a familial disease had upset not only her but also her husband and grandparents. This was seen to be an important factor and although blame had not been apportioned to any of the relatives there was, nevertheless, a suspicion that somebody was at fault and mother was accepting the blame. Her husband had little to say but his child's mental retardation had been a great disappointment to him.

When the family was seen by the genetic counsellor the clinical findings in the child coupled with the information obtained from the hospital records made it clear that the diagnosis was correct. Adenoma sebaceum, or tuberose sclerosis, is a well recognised condition characterised by three major features: mental retardation, epilepsy and a peculiar facial rash which gives the disease its name. This rash is situated on the cheeks or over the bridge of the nose and resembles acne. As with other dominantly inherited conditions not every patient who inherits the gene manifests all the features and varying degrees of severity or expressivity are common. The child had developed a peculiar form of epilepsy early in life with so-called infantile spasms, later progressing to grand mal epilepsy. His facial skin was normal but he was obviously considerably retarded. Mother was of low normal intelligence but certainly not retarded and had never had epilepsy. She did, however, have a very marked and typical rash of adenoma sebaceum and when she was examined more thoroughly was found to have depigmented patches in her skin, the so-called shagreen patches. These are seen in many affected patients.

There was no doubt, therefore, about the diagnosis and little doubt that the condition had been passed from mother to the child. During discussions about the inheritance, however, the point was repeatedly made that no-one is responsible for their genetic inheritance. It was emphasised to mother and father that all of us inherit some abnormal genes from our parents and that we cannot pick and choose which genes we will have and which we won't have. It was difficult for mother initially to understand how she could have the disease in only this mild form and even more difficult for her to understand how it was that both her parents were normal. It had to be explained that her disease was the result of a mutation in her parents' gametes and that she had then passed the gene to her child. This was difficult and took time and patience on everyone's part. Since tuberose sclerosis is inherited in a dominant fashion it was explained to the parents that the chance of their having another affected child was high, 50/50 or 1 in 2. Their immediate reaction was that they would certainly not contemplate having further children. This response was the result of the high risk quoted and the fact that the parents considered the disease to be extremely burdensome.

At all stages the interview had to be conducted with an awareness of the psychological implications and the need for facts to be presented simply and clearly. When encouraged to talk about their problem the parents admitted to having had considerable depression and rejection to their infant when they learned of his mental retardation. They spent fully an hour discussing a number of aspects and during that time the genetic nurse who had interviewed them was present and made some attempt to assess what questions were left unasked. She also attempted to assess how much of the information given was being understood and its possible effect. It was thought advisable to see mother's parents and although both were said to be free of any evidence of adenoma sebaceum this needed to be confirmed. The health visitor made arrangements to visit them at their home, having been assured by mother that they would not be upset by such a visit and would probably welcome it. The consultands were given an appointment for a further interview in six weeks' time. In the interim mother was visited by the health visitor. The risk figure that had been quoted was apparently understood and she was still fairly adamant that she did not want any further children. Her husband had not said very much about the interview and his wife suspected he was blaming her even more than previously. It was not possible to see him with his wife before their next appointment. Mother's sister was anxious to come to the clinic and arrangements were made for the health visitor attached to the clinic to visit her general practitioner who subsequently agreed to refer her to the counselling clinic.

When the couple next attended there were additional points discussed. Mother wanted to know if another child who inherited the gene would be more or less severely affected with the disease. It was explained that there was no way of determining this but for practical purposes it would be sensible to assume that the child might be at least as seriously affected as the other sibling. It had been established that mother's parents were free of the disease when seen at home and the opportunity was taken to make brief reference once again to spontaneous mutation. It was considered highly unlikely that the affected child would ever marry and have children. Mother volunteered the information that she had seen her family doctor about contraceptive advice and she and her husband remained adamant that they did not want any further children. Both seemed to benefit from the discussion and were very grateful for the information and help provided. The genetic nurse arranged for the health visitor to visit the family again in a few months. This would be a useful opportunity to reinforce the information and to enquire how the family had reacted to the counselling session.

Mother's sister was eventually seen. She did have a facial rash and it was difficult to be sure whether or not this was adenoma sebaceum. She was of average intelligence and had never had epilepsy. As she was planning to marry it was important to establish if she had the disease. She was referred to a dermatologist and eventually required a skin biopsy before being reassured that she did not have adenoma sebaceum. It was explained, therefore, that since she did not have the disease she could not pass it on to her children.

This family illustrates all of the main principles in genetic counselling practice. If the diagnosis had not been a firm one it would have been necessary to enlist the aid of any expert who could help. Family pedigree information was collected and had this been inadequate further home visits would have been necessary. Other family members were examined and the mode of inheritance clearly identified. The emotional impact of the disease on the patients had been assessed and the information given in a way which took account of this. It was also important to appreciate their educational attainments and intellectual abilities. It is not an easy matter to discuss genes and modes of inheritance with people of limited educational background but it can be successful provided the language used is kept simple and diagrams or other aids used.

The same approach can be used for any other dominantly inherited condition. The risk to the offspring of a person with such a disease is 50/50 or 1 in 2. Sometimes the information is requested about the risk to the next generation. The answer to this is $\frac{1}{2} \times \frac{1}{2} = \frac{1}{4}$. This risk will obviously become $\frac{1}{2}$ again if at any time the apparently unaffected parent develops evidence of the disease. In the family with tylosis shown in Fig. 6.2 the disease appeared in five generations. It is characterised by marked thickening of the skin of the palms and soles. In a few patients oesophageal carcinoma also occurs later in life. The consultand was getting married and wanted to know the risks to her children. Her cousin, also affected, had two normal children. This was fortunate; another cousin, had two affected children as did his mother. The risk to the consultand's children was 50/50 and this was easily understood by her. She had a very adequate demonstration of the inheritance pattern in her family.

A considerable number of genetic disorders may not present at birth but appear at varying times throughout life. Some of these may be dominantly inherited and Huntington's Chorea is the best known example. Because of its late onset, usually in early or middle years, those individuals who have inherited the responsible gene may have already completed their family before developing symptoms. Unfortunately, there is no test at present which will detect the presymptomatic carrier of the gene and treatment of the condition is not

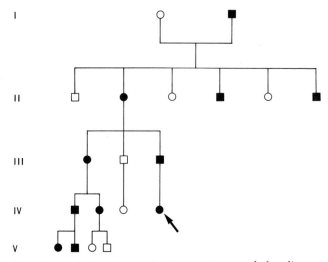

Fig. 6.2 Tylosis. The vertical transmission of the disease affecting either sex is very typical of dominant inheritance.

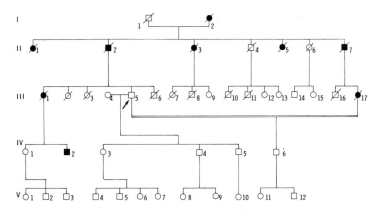

Fig. 6.3 'Out of the frying pan into the fire'. The consultand III·5, was 74 years old when he attended the clinic. His father and other family members died from Huntington's Chorea. However he was very healthy and had no evidence of the disease, nor did any of the children to his first wife. It was unlikely therefore that he had inherited the abnormal gene. He had remarried and his second wife was his cousin whose father had died from the disease. This woman developed the condition and died. Our consultand's son IV·6 is therefore at 50/50 risk of inheriting the gene. The children have currently a 1 : 4 risk.

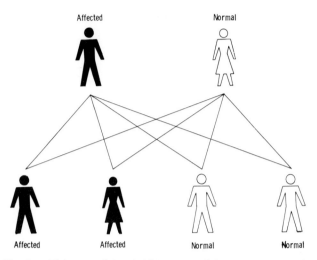

Fig. 6.4 This type of visual aid is very useful in genetic counselling. It demonstrates dominant inheritance and is usually easily understood.

satisfactory. The disease is characterised by psychiatric symptoms in addition to the abnormal choreiform movements from which it derives its name. Most patients have symptoms before the age of 50 years, but it may be later or earlier. In common with psychiatric conditions, Huntington's Chorea may produce very great familial upset. For example, it is not unusual to find considerable reluctance on the part of some families to discuss details of affected relatives. Fortunately, this attitude is less common now than previously. It is worth remembering that in the past the medical profession avoided discussion of the genetic implications although these have been known for many years.

Since there is no means of detecting the presence of the gene before it produces signs of the disease any offspring of an affected person has to be given a 50/50 risk of developing the condition. In addition, as in other similar situations any children of a person at risk also has a 50/50 risk of inheriting the responsible gene. It is possible to reduce the risk to the non-symptomatic son or daughter of an affected person as they age, but unfortunately complete reassurance can only be given much later in life.

Recessive Inheritance
Fig. 6.5 is the pedigree of a family in which two girls were born with the adrenogenital syndrome. The most common variety of this disease, due to a deficiency of an enzyme, 21-hydroxylase, is characterised

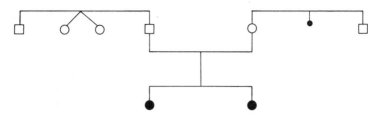

Fig. 6.5 Adrenogenital Syndrome. Both daughters affected.

by changes in the female genitalia and electrolyte disturbances. The genital changes may be so marked as to cause confusion about the child's sex at birth. The clitoris is much larger than usual and may resemble a penis; the labia are often fused and may look like a poorly developed scrotum. At any stage in the immediate neo-natal period or subsequently the affected children may develop gross disturbance of their electrolyte metabolism with collapse due to adrenal failure. On diagnosis the children are treated with cortisone and they have to remain on this for the rest of their life. The mother of the two affected children was coping with difficulty. She had a constant and very troublesome anxiety about her daughters' genitalia and frequently needed reassurance that they were normal females. This aspect of the problem was made apparent by the referring doctor's letter and it was causing considerable strain in the family as well as difficulties in the management of the children. This anxiety is very common and may persist for some years. The life threatening electrolyte disturbances and the need for frequent hospital attendances make this disease a very burdensome one. With proper management, however, the children can live a normal life.

At the initial interview Mrs C.'s anxiety about her daughters' sexual development was very apparent and it was obvious that this was an important factor for the whole family. Neither mother nor father had any basic biological knowledge and although they had already been given some facts about the disease their knowledge appeared to be very inadequate; mother still had many misconceptions about the whole problem. There was no history of any other significant disease in the family. Mother and father were both healthy and it was difficult for them to understand why it was that they had children affected by this disorder. The oldest affected child was ten and mother had been told of the risk in further pregnancies. Nevertheless, the information was either not fully comprehended or was ignored, and as a consequence the second affected child was born. The parents felt that they had not been made sufficiently aware of this risk and had not discussed this aspect in sufficient detail. After a prolonged discussion about the basic physiology and the mechanism of recessive inheritance they were told that the recurrence risk was 25 per cent or 1 in 4.

At their next visit they seemed to have clearly grasped the figures quoted and mother then enquired about the risks to her son of having a child with a similar problem. It was possible to be very reassuring to her about this. It was explained that although her son might have inherited the gene carried by herself and her husband, the only way he could have an affected child would be if he were unlucky enough to marry someone carrying the same abnormal gene. The chances of his doing this depended on the frequency of the gene in the population and this in turn could be calculated approximately if the incidence of the disease is known. The principles underlying this type of calculation were initially propounded by two mathematicians, Hardy and Weinberg, and using their formula the gene frequency of this particular syndrome was calculated to be approximately 1 in 100. As there is only a 1 in 4 chance of an affected child when both parents are carriers, the eventual risk is, therefore, 1 in 400, i.e. $1/100 \times 1/4 = 1/400$. This risk is low and the parents interpreted it as considerable reassurance.

Mother's basic anxiety about her children's genitalia did not lessen despite the discussion. It was concluded, however, that both she and her husband were now in a position to make an informed decision about further children. It was explained that they would be notified if there was any further advance in the prenatal diagnosis of the condition. Measurement of liquor 17 α-hydroxy-progesterone may prove to be helpful in this respect.

This family demonstrates once again the important principles underlying successful genetic counselling. The diagnosis was firm and the prognosis of the disease fully appreciated by the genetic counselling staff. The inheritance pattern was clear and a 25 per cent recurrence risk for recessive disease was conveyed as a high risk. For the purposes of counselling, risks greater than 1 in 10 are thought of as high, risks between 1 in 10 and 1 in 20 as moderate, and risks less than 1 in 20 as low. In all cases it is important to draw the attention of the consultands to the fact that any pregnancy has a 1/40 risk of a serious congenital abnormality. It is against this background risk that all other risks are assessed. However it is equally important to remember that the risk is only one of a number of factors which are involved in ultimate decision making. In this couple the considerable anxiety overlay was seen as presenting an obstacle to a discussion of the clinical and genetic aspects of the disease. Mother needed a lot of time to talk through her various problems and it was concluded that although she had been given some information after the birth of her first child it seemed likely that insufficient time was spent with her and she failed to become completely aware of the problem.

Fig. 6.6 shows a pedigree of an immigrant Pakistani family. As followers of the Muslim faith they had been brought up to an acceptance of first cousin marriages and as can be seen from the pedigree there is a considerable degree of consanguinity. In this family three children died very soon after birth from what appeared to be a biochemical disturbance. The couple had five children in total, two of whom were alive and well. Post-mortem examination of one of the infants confirmed that the cause of death was Pompe's Disease. It seemed highly probable from the information given that two previous infants had also died from this disease. This condition results from a metabolic disturbance and is characterised by the deposition of glycogen in muscle tissue, particularly the heart and liver. Death normally occurs early in life. This disease is one of a number which may be diagnosed prenatally. Fortunately, the couple spoke reasonable English and were able to comprehend an explanation about the disease and the basic genetic principles. It was explained in detail that the condition was recessively inherited and that this implied that both parents carried the responsible gene. It was stressed that this would not affect them clinically but that affected children developed the disease because of their homozygous state. The basic facts of consanguinity were demonstrated and discussion encouraged. It was explained that as first cousins, sharing

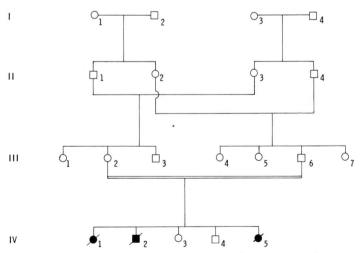

Fig. 6.6   Pompe's Disease. A rare recessive disease segregating in a consanguinous marriage.

one-eighth of their total complement of genes, they were at considerably higher risk than the general population of carrying the same abnormal gene and hence manifesting this rare disease. These principles apply to any first cousin marriage and the only dangers of such a marriage rest on this fact. Despite the cultural differences, mother and father were anxious to discuss prenatal diagnosis. It was assessed, however, that this would be best done at another session and in the meantime it was arranged for the health visitor to see mother at home and to advise her about contraception. Both parents accepted a 1 in 4 risk of another affected child as high and seemed prepared to accept advice on how this could be avoided. Mother did not want further children but it was more difficult to assess father's views on this matter. Although he had one living son he did express a desire to have another male family member. In view of the cultural differences the effect of genetic counselling on our immigrant population needs further study and research.

At a subsequent session all the details of prenatal diagnosis were explained and diagrams were used to explain amniocentesis. The parents were told that only a few specialised laboratories were capable of making a prenatal diagnosis in this condition and that they would require warning if and when mother decided to start another pregnancy. There was doubt expressed about the termination of an affected infant and this aspect of the management had to be stressed and re-stressed. By the conclusion of the second interview

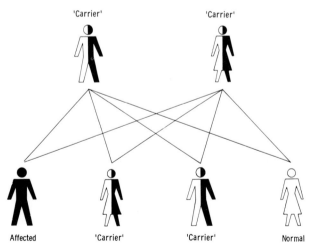

Fig. 6.7   This helps the consultand understand recessive inheritance.

it was agreed by the counselling staff that both parents were aware of the risk to another child, understood to some extent what was involved in prenatal diagnosis and were sufficiently responsible to communicate with the clinic again, if and when they decided to have another child. Their decision was reached as in the other cases on the basis of information and discussion.

X-linked Inheritance

Fig. 6.8 shows a family in which male infants have suffered from muscular dystrophy of the Duchenne variety in different generations. The pedigree shows clearly the transmission of the disease from the female carrier to her sons and confirms the absence of male to male transmission. It is important to remember that there are various types of muscular dystrophy but the Duchenne variety is the most distressing. It normally becomes apparent by the age of 3–5 years, progresses slowly and death usually occurs at about the age of 16–17. Such prolonged disease produces very great distress in the parents and by any standards must be seen as very burdensome. In all genetic counselling problems it is important to make some assessment of the burden of the condition. Some disorders may have a very high recurrence risk but very little inconvenience, e.g. incurved little fingers, clinodactyly; this may be dominantly inherited. The burden of the condition, however, is slight or negligible. Other abnormalities with more serious consequences may produce very much more emotional distress. Infants born with anencephaly die soon after birth; the distress here is severe but hopefully limited. In Duchenne muscular dystrophy the distress is both severe and con-

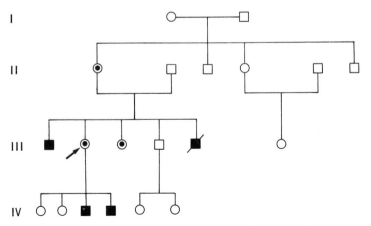

Fig. 6.8   Duchenne Muscular Dystrophy (see text).

tinuing and the burden is a very heavy one. As the child's debility increases so the parents' distress increases until his eventual death brings the whole sad episode to a close. Subsequently, many parents continue to grieve for months or even years. It is important to try and assess the distress resulting from or likely to result from disease to ensure that adequate help can be given.

Mrs X., the consultand, had two male children affected by the disease and two daughters, clinically normal. In addition she had two affected brothers, one of whom had already died from the disease. One of her sons, aged eight, was showing marked weakness. The other boy was only four but was already demonstrating the typical enlargement of his calf muscles. Both daughters were older, in their teens, and both very aware of the increasing disability in their brothers. At the initial interview the basic mechanism of inheritance was explained in detail and the couple were already aware of the need to establish the carrier status of their daughters. Mrs X., who was on the contraceptive pill, was adamant that she did not want further children and she and her husband had made this firm commitment some time previously. Family pedigree information is very important and from the details received about this particular family it was obvious that mother was an obligatory carrier, having had two affected sons. Her serum creatine kinase levels averaged 120 iu/l on three specimens, the normal levels are between 0–50 iu/l. Her oldest daughter, aged 13, had an average of 98 iu/l. This increased her probability of being a carrier. The other daughter, aged 11, averaged 30 iu/l and this increased the chance of her not being a carrier. However, this biochemical test, like many other investigations, is not infallible and unfortunately in about 25 per cent of carrier females a false-negative value may be obtained. The affected boys had creatine kinase levels of 1500 iu/l and 1400 iu/l, as expected when the patient suffers from the disease.

In this family it is useful to know that mother is an obligatory carrier and her biochemical results can be compared with those of her daughters. In other families where mother may have only one affected son and no affected brothers or nephews, it may be more difficult to decide on the carrier status of females. Help is available from several techniques but it is essential to combine the pedigree and biochemical information to obtain a final probability of the carrier state.

If this couple had wished to have another pregnancy then the possibility of fetal sexing would have been discussed. Amniocentesis at about 14–16 weeks of pregnancy can provide fetal cells and a karyotype can determine fetal sex. Such a test has a high degree of reliability and accuracy. If the infant is male then mother has the

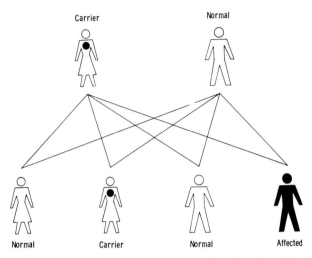

Fig. 6.9   Visual aid to explain how carrier females of sex linked recessive disease may have affected sons and carrier daughters.

option, if she wishes, of terminating the male pregnancy and taking only females to term. This is not a solution that appeals to everyone and obviously some aborted male infants may be normal. In addition, each daughter has a 50/50 chance of being a carrier and many couples are naturally concerned about carrier daughters having the same problems as themselves. For these very practical reasons some couples may not wish to adopt this course of action. Others, because of their religious or moral principles, may also not welcome this type of help. Nevertheless, it is one means of ensuring that a couple may have a child with the guarantee that she will not have Duchenne muscular dystrophy. Unfortunately, there is no guarantee that the daughter will not have some other problem and it is necessary to make this point when discussing the matter with the parents. This approach could be seen to be reasonable in the case of the older woman who has already lost one or two sons with this disease. If her childbearing years are very limited then selective termination of pregnancy would permit her to have an unaffected female child.

Although parents are rightly very aware of the problems facing their offspring it is worthwhile stating that by the time a carrier daughter is of childbearing age there may well be changes in our management of the disease. Naturally, this cannot be guaranteed but it does help to put things into perspective. Recent advances in the technique of fetoscopy have enabled a few male fetuses affected by Duchenne dystrophy to be recognised sufficiently early in pregnancy

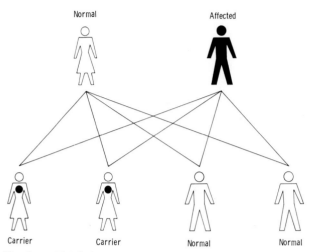

Fig. 6.10   This helps to explain how a man suffering from sex linked recessive disease has carrier daughters. All his sons are normal.

for termination to be offered. The fetoscope is an instrument which allows the fetus to be visually examined. It is a flexible tube in which there are a large number of mirrors relaying images to the examiner's eye. Unfortunately, inserting the fetoscope into the uterus is not as simple as amniocentesis and the risk of miscarriage is higher than with other procedures. By being able to identify the fetal end of the placenta it is possible to obtain a specimen of fetal blood and to measure the creatine kinase level. In a small number of fetuses affected by Duchenne muscular dystrophy in which this technique has been used, the creatine kinase has shown the expected high levels. It is not yet clear, however, whether all the affected fetuses will show high diagnostic levels and further research is needed. It would seem possible that advances in technology and particularly refinements in fetoscopy will occur. This should result in improvement in the management of this type of disease as well as others. In thalassaemia intrauterine diagnosis of the affected fetus has been successful in a considerable number of cases.

Multifactorial Inheritance

The most common of the diseases considered to be multifactorial in origin is spina bifida with meningomyelocele. This condition is part of the spectrum of neural tube abnormalities which also includes anencephaly and some cases of hydrocephalus. They will be dealt

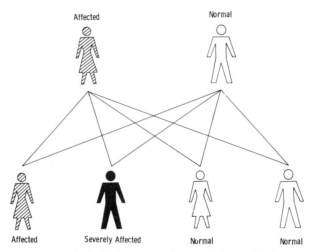

Fig. 6.11 X-linked dominant disease. The male is more severely affected. A helpful picture for consultands.

with in more detail under prenatal diagnosis. Hare-lip and cleft palate is also a common problem and Mr and Mrs P. were referred to the genetic counselling clinic because they had two sons born with this distressing abnormality. Although the parents were initially very concerned about their children's appearance the operative repair was successful and they were pleased with the outcome. However, they had been through a great deal of stress and their children needed several admissions to hospital for operations. They were anxious, therefore, to know about recurrence risks in subsequent pregnancies. There was no history of similar problems on either side of the family and both mother and father were healthy and had no physical abnormalities. Mother had been well during pregnancy and the only drugs she had taken were oral iron and an antacid for heartburn. On examination, the children had no evidence of any other physical abnormalities, both had a fine scar from the repair of the hare-lip and their speech was progressing well.

Whereas single gene abnormalities have a high risk of recurrence, multifactorial conditions, when there has only been one affected sib, have a low recurrence risk. With normal parents and one male child only affected, the recurrence risk of hare-lip and cleft palate in approximately 1 in 40 to 1 in 50. With two affected male children the risk for a further affected sibling is approximately 1 in 12. Because males are affected more frequently than females, the recurrence risk would have been slightly higher if one of the affected children had been a girl. The reason for this is that when the less common sex is involved there is presumed to be a stronger genetic component and hence a slightly higher risk for another affected sib. This risk was considered high by the parents and they decided to have no further children.

The recurrence risk for conditions which we have listed as multi-factorial in origin are said to be empiric. They are not calculated on genetic principles like the single gene disorders but instead the recurrence figures are estimated by examining large numbers of families in which the disease has occurred. Empiric risks are also quoted for some other conditions including the chromosomal disorders and may be quoted in some forms of congenital heart disease; the varieties not associated with particular syndromes. Some heart lesions, however, may be associated with well-recognised single gene conditions and the recurrence risk may be high. For example, the combination of a septal defect and thumb abnormalities constitutes the Holt-Oram Syndrome. This is dominantly inherited and if one or other parent has some sign of the disease then the recurrence risk will be 50/50. In Marfan's Syndrome, the patient may have abnormalities of the aorta in addition to the 'spider' fingers and toes. This condition is also dominantly inherited and the risk to an affected parent is 50/50.

Fig. 6.12 is of another family which was referred to the counselling clinic because the child had hare-lip and cleft palate and the parents were anxious to know the risk for further children. There was no other family history and one other sibling, a daughter, was said to be

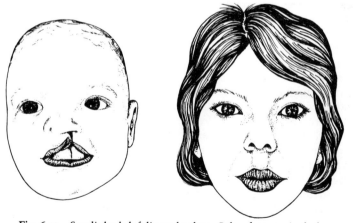

Fig. 6.12 Sex-linked cleft lip and palate. Other features include telecanthus and hypospadias. The carrier mother demonstrates the telecanthus (wide spacing of eyes due to increase in tissue at root of nose).

normal. On examination at the clinic it was confirmed that this child's problem was not just cleft lip and palate. His eyes were widely spaced and he also had a mild degree of hypospadias. During discussion with mother it was noticed that she also had wide spacing of her eyes and this family trait had been noticed by her husband. It was obviously something that was accepted by the family and in mother added to her general attractive appearance.

In this situation, however, the association of the cleft-lip and palate with these other features suggested the diagnosis of a syndrome referred to as the BBB Syndrome. This unhelpful title is made up of the first letter of the surnames of the first three families described. It is probably better labelled the telecanthus-hypospadias syndrome. Telecanthus is the term given to wide spacing of the eyes due to an increase in the soft tissue mass at the root of the nose. Many affected male infants have other associated abnormalities in addition to hare-lip and cleft palate. This condition may be X-linked and the female carrier may show the telecanthus which is present in her affected son. This was the case in mother and it was explained to her that any male she had would have a 50/50 chance of a similar abnormality. Daughters of the carrier female appear to escape the more serious abnormalities. In some cases of this syndrome mental retardation is also present but this particular child appeared to be developing normally. One could not guarantee, however, that another affected child would also have a normal intellect and this point had to be gently stressed. This case again illustrates the importance of thorough examination and an awareness that the diagnosis suggested in the referral letter may not be the correct or the only one. Occasionally, hare-lip and cleft palate may be associated with small pits in the lower lip. One or other parent without hare-lip or cleft palate may have similar pits and it is important to examine the parents of affected children carefully. This finding suggests that the condition is in fact dominantly inherited and the association of the lip pits, hare-lip and palate abnormalities is referred to as Van der Woude's Syndrome.

In all the conditions considered to be of multifactorial origin it is important to be constantly on the lookout for possible environmental factors. It is to be hoped that all pregnant women will be encouraged to keep an accurate record of medicines and drugs taken not only in the early stages of pregnancy but also later on. Recently there has been a suggestion that the drug, Epanutin, might cause cleft palate or hare-lip and in addition produce shortening of the phalanges. Further proof of this association is required but the suggestion does highlight the need to use drugs with caution. In all congenital abnormalities of unknown aetiology it is important to

take a detailed history of mother's pregnancy with particular reference to drug ingestion. Unfortunately, many mothers forget which
drugs they may have taken in the early stages of pregnancy. Since
organogenesis in the fetus occurs in the first three months it is at the
beginning of this period when drugs may have their maximum
teratogenic effect.

Although the number of drugs capable of producing congenital
abnormalities is small there is the possibility that some with teratogenic effects are being overlooked. It may also be important for us
to know the exact period of drug ingestion. Some teratogenic sub-
stances might be taken with impunity on day 21 and 22 but if taken
as a limb bud is appearing during the second month there could be
serious consequences. The genetic counselling clinic provides a useful opportunity for health education in these matters and is an aspect
of the work that should not be overlooked. It should be helpful to
any woman to discuss this aspect of her pregnancy and if she does have
to have medicines these should be known to be safe. She should also
be discouraged from going to the chemist for proprietary prepara-
tions either for the management of heartburn, backache or other
ailments. As far as possible, her symptoms should be treated by her
family doctor. In addition it is important that the primary health
care team are aware of the need to use only those medicines which do
not have any teratogenic effect and which have been tried over the
years.

Chromosomal Abnormalities

Down's Syndrome like the neural tube defects, is a very commonly
referred problem. Over 90 per cent of children with this abnormality
have the classical trisomy 21 with three instead of two chromosomes
of Group G. As we have seen this abnormality arises as a result of
non-disjunction during meiosis, more commonly in the female than
in the male.

In a family referred to the clinic mother was 23, her husband 25
and both were in good health. They had had no illnesses of note, the
pregnancy was uneventful and the birth of the child with Down's
Syndrome was completely unexpected. Surprisingly there was a
family history of this disease. Father had a female cousin who died
from congenital heart disease associated with Down's Syndrome.
She had died early in life and the information only came to light when
father made enquiries about the family pedigree. Neither his wife nor
he had any knowledge of the disease and the birth of their affected
daughter came as a great shock. Both parents were surprised at the
obvious reluctance of their relatives to disclose the details of the

affected cousin. This is a common problem and previous generations were not encouraged to discuss these issues. In many cases they may actively suppress information which may be pertinent.

The child's physical appearance was typical of the disease and the diagnosis was suspected within a short time of delivery. Mother was concerned from a very early stage and was told the diagnosis within 12 hours of delivery. At the counselling clinic she remembered this occasion as being one of the most unhappy in her life. She had only a hazy recollection of the events of the next few days but her husband confirmed that she had been shocked to the extent of not wanting to speak. She apparently wept a great deal, questioned the diagnosis and wanted to leave the hospital before her official time of discharge. Her husband did his best to be supportive despite the fact that he was also very upset. Both parents were quite prepared to talk about this unhappy period and were allowed to do so during the counselling session. Not only had they been acutely depressed but they also had strong feelings of personal recrimination. On occasions they tended to blame one another and felt angry at almost everyone for no reason other than the fact that this had happened to them. They could remember their feelings very distinctly and although they had improved they were still depressed. Fortunately, their marriage was a sound one and they were able to give one another some support.

This sequence of events is predictable after the birth of a handicapped child and particularly so when the child's handicap includes mental retardation. Most parents are aware of the significance of Down's Syndrome and even with sensitivity and tact it is very difficult for the doctor giving this information to prevent considerable emotional upset. In most cases, one or hopefully, both parents begin to improve again within 2–3 months of the delivery. At that stage they normally begin to think about re-organising their lives to meet the needs of the child and to think about the future. It is at this stage only that genetic counselling can be of any help. If parents are referred to a counselling clinic while they are still suffering remorse and depression detailed discussion about the future is usually unhelpful. It may be very difficult for them to understand the chromosomal basis of their child's problem if they are still looking for relief from their anxiety or for someone to take their problem from them. In addition they may not be capable of understanding recurrence risks or details of amniocentesis. There is now increasing medical awareness of the need to delay referral until the worst of this emotional upset is over. On occasions, however, pressure from very anxious parents may result in their coming to the clinic soon after the birth of the affected child. The clinic team and the parents have to cope as best they can with this situation.

This couple had come to terms with their problem. They were shown a karyotype and the basis of trisomy 21 was discussed. It was explained that the recurrence risk was low, probably not greater than 1 in 100 but increasing as mother aged. The unexpected occurrence of a paternal cousin with the condition did not influence the risk they were given but it did emphasise that other people may have the same problem. It is useful to demonstrate the increasing risk with advancing maternal age by means of a diagram and a steeply rising curve from 35 onwards tends to be a more effective demonstration than simple percentage figures. Although the risk of recurrence is small the burden of looking after a mentally handicapped child is great. Many couples consider it greater than looking after a physically handicapped child and for this reason many mothers are anxious to have amniocentesis. In most cases this will normally be reassuring and recurrences are rare. The indication for amniocentesis in this situation is basically maternal anxiety. The details of this procedure need to be explained and the parents are told about its timing, risks and other aspects. By the end of the session they should have a better understanding of their child's problem but it is usually necessary for them to be seen on more than one occasion.

Although most cases of Down's Syndrome result from trisomy 21 the pedigree in Fig. 6.13 is of a family in which Down's Syndrome has occurred as a result of a translocation. About 8 per cent of all

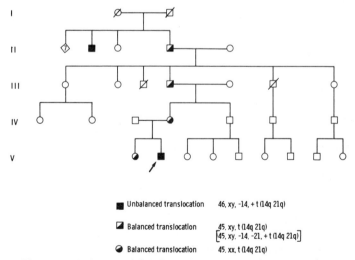

■ Unbalanced translocation   46, xy, -14, + t (14q 21q)

◨ Balanced translocation   45, xy, t (14q 21q)
                              [45, xy, -14, -21, + t (14q 21q)]

◖ Balanced translocation   45, xx, t (14q 21q)

Fig. 6.13   Pedigree of family with 14.21 translocation. The karyotype shorthand is shown. In line 2 the balanced translocation may be written in either of the two ways demonstrated.

patients with Down's Syndrome have this type of chromosomal rearrangement. The particular translocation in this family is between chromosomes No. 14 and 21 and this was first found with the birth of the propositus marked with the arrow. The child had all the usual features of Down's Syndrome. When this condition was found to have resulted from a translocation then it became important to examine the karyotype of the parents and other siblings. As it turned out mother was found to be a carrier of the translocation and so also was a three year old sister. Both were completely normal physically and mentally and their translocation was therefore balanced. More extensive checks on the family confirmed that mother's father was a carrier and someone eventually produced old photographs which showed a male child with Down's Syndrome in generation II. The photograph was taken in 1904! In this type of investigation it is very important that a full explanation is given to everyone who volunteers to have their chromosomes examined. It is also necessary to ensure that they are given a full explanation of the findings both normal and abnormal. There may be some difficulty in ensuring that carriers of the balanced translocation appreciate that this will not affect them in any way physically or mentally. This point needs to be emphasised and stated as frequently as seems necessary. The preventative aspects of the findings should also be stressed. It can be explained to the carriers of the translocation that by knowing their karyotype it is now possible to prevent the birth of a further affected child. For example, in this pedigree the little girl of three will have a risk of about 1 in 8 of having a child with an unbalanced form of the translocation and hence Down's Syndrome. With prenatal diagnosis, however, she can have the option of termination if the fetus is shown to be affected. Where the male is shown to be a carrier, the risk to his offspring is less but nevertheless his wife should avail herself of amniocentesis and prenatal diagnosis. When parents have no knowledge of biology it is not easy for them to understand a discussion about chromosomes and chromosomal rearrangements. However, most can be helped by the use of diagrams or karyotypes and a book full of these is always on hand in most clinics. It is very important that the counselling team appreciate that a mother or father may say they understand, out of politeness, when in fact they clearly do not. It is for this reason that time must be spent and more than one interview is nearly always necessary. The information must be understood and this will often mean the avoidance of scientific terminology and a willingness on the part of the counsellor to encourage simple questions. One result of this technique is to demonstrate to the counselling team the gross deficiencies in their own knowledge! It also affords them the opportunity of learning the type of language that would be most useful in answering particular questions. Before a mother may have begun to grapple with the problem of chromosomes she may want to be reassured that she has not been responsible for her child's problem. She may have very strong feelings of responsibility and unless one is sensitive to her problem the counselling session may be ineffective.

Developmental Defects

It is not unusual for children with various clusters of physical abnormalities to be referred to the genetic counselling clinic for diagnosis. It is assumed because such referrals are common, that the clinic may be able to recognise and label a particular condition. This in turn would help in the subsequent management and understanding of the disease. Infants or children with abnormalities of the face, for example, low set ears, down-turned eyes or wide-spacing of the eyes, are often referred to as dysmorphic or of having dysmorphic features. In fact, some of these features noticed at birth gradually disappear as the child matures and it is important not to place too

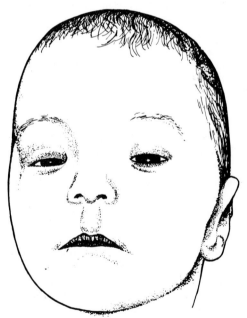

Fig. 6.14   Smith-Lemli-Opitz Syndrome. Face is characteristic; bilateral ptosis, upturned nostrils, long philtrum (from nostrils to upper lip). Child is retarded and has hypospadias.

much importance on any single feature. Many of us have slight deviations from the normal; some more than others! However, some specific groups of abnormalities may be recognised as comprising a definite well recognised condition. Down's anomaly is a very good example of this and so are many of the classical chromosomal conditions.

Mrs X. was referred to the counselling clinic because her child was found at birth to have an unusual facial appearance in addition to generalised hypotonia and subsequent developmental delay. There was no family history of any other abnormal babies and mother and father were both healthy and of normal intelligence. On examination the child showed generalised hypotonia and obvious developmental delay. He also had a mild degree of hypospadias. His facial appearance was odd and on analysis this was the result of slight ptosis of both upper eyelids, slight upturning of the nostrils and a long upper lip. All these features when combined constitute the Smith-Lemli-Opitz Syndrome. This condition is well described in the literature and is recognised to be recessively inherited. The parents, therefore, had to be given a high recurrence risk for subsequent pregnancies and a full and detailed discussion of the basis of recessive inheritance was necessary. Having a label for the disease did not alter the outlook although it did imply that further investigations were unnecessary. Not all dysmorphic infants are so rapidly categorised. Many babies with dysmorphic features are referred for diagnosis and the parents for genetic counselling. When a full clinical examination does not add anything further to the problem then it is necessary to consider further investigations such as a karyotype, x-rays and biochemical tests. It is also very important that the counselling staff have access to the vast literature which has accumulated on clinical genetics and congenital anomalies. Despite investigations and a thorough literature search the diagnosis may still be in doubt in a considerable number of patients. It is therefore, very difficult to quote an accurate recurrence risk. Fortunately it is a useful generalisation in genetic counselling work that the more difficult it is to put a specific label on a condition, usually the less likely the risk of recurrence. Like every other generalisation it may not be correct in specific instances.

In the family in Fig. 6.15 the third child, a male infant, was found to have a congenital heart lesion shortly after birth. Initially this was thought to be a ventricular septal defect but subsequently turned out to be a mild aortic stenosis. The child failed to grow adequately although there was no evidence that his heart was failing. It was only when the whole family was collected and examined closely that mother was found to have a similar aortic valve abnormality and without her high heels was only 4' 10" tall. Facially she resembled her son very strongly and the diagnosis was almost certainly Noonan's Syndrome, a dominantly inherited form of heart disease. The risk to further offspring was 50/50. She had two daughters both of whom appeared to be normal and were of normal height.

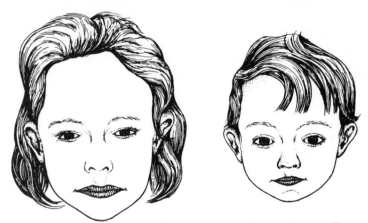

Fig. 6.15   Noonan's Syndrome. Congenital heart lesion, small stature and slightly odd facial appearance. Both mother and child had wide spaced eyes, narrow palpebral fissures and prominent ears.

Fig. 6.16   Genetic counselling should be conducted in a calm relaxed atmosphere. There should be no coercion on the part of the counsellor! At least not often. . .

The recognition of specific patterns of congenital abnormalities is a very important function of the genetic counselling clinic. Since this work tends to be involved with the total family there is a greater opportunity to observe and identify familial transmission of disease. In some cases a child may be thought to be the only affected person in a family. On closer examination of the parents, however, one of them may be found to have minor manifestations of the same condition. This varying expressivity has already been discussed under dominant diseases. It can certainly present problems to the counsellor and emphasises the need to see the whole family when possible.

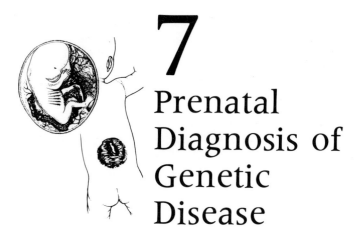

7
Prenatal Diagnosis of Genetic Disease

There is nothing new in attempting to forecast the outcome of a pregnancy. Every practising nurse will be familiar with some suggested method of determining fetal sex by the state of mother's pregnancy, the time of conception and even how much abdominal enlargement there is during the pregnancy. Since there is an approximately 50/50 chance of being correct it is not too surprising that a great deal of folklore has accumulated over the centuries. There have also developed a great number of old wives' or old midwives' tales about the influence of prenatal events on the baby's physical state and even intellectual ability. It is only over the past decade, however, that prenatal diagnosis, not only of fetal sex, but of some fetal diseases, has become an established part of medical practice. This development may be seen as one of the most interesting advances in perinatal medicine during the past few decades. In addition to preventing the birth of abnormal children this technique has also given tremendous stimulus to the growth of genetic counselling services and to increasing interest in the application of genetics to medical problems. Prior to the advent of prenatal diagnostic techniques genetic counselling consisted of assessing a risk and then ensuring that this risk was understood by the parents. Since nothing further could be done in most situations it was then up to the parents to decide whether or not to have children. However, the ability to diagnose fetal disease now means that genetic counselling need no longer end in impass in certain situations.

Because most services have developed *ad hoc*, the facilities for prenatal diagnosis are not uniformly available throughout the

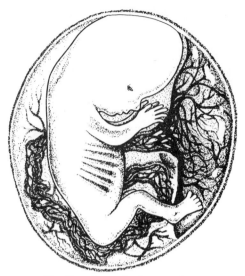

Fig. 7.1   Second trimester fetus.

country. However, there is likely to be an increasing demand for this type of help and it can be assumed, despite the many inherent problems, that it is here to stay. The number of conditions which may be diagnosed *in utero* is steadily increasing and both nursing staff and doctors may find difficulty in keeping up to date with the advances.

Table 7.1 shows the various methods of prenatal diagnosis. Examination of the fetus relies on a variety of techniques basically divided into those which attempt to observe the fetus directly and those which study fetal well-being from examination of liquor amnii, mother's blood or urine. Direct fetal imaging may be by x-ray or ultrasonography. Standard radiography may reveal a serious skeletal disease or gross abnormalities of fetal skull development. Unfortunately, by the time fetal bones are radiologically distinct, termination of pregnancy is difficult and late, usually after 24 weeks of gestation. There is also concern about the use of standard x-ray techniques because of the radiation hazard to mother's ovaries.

The newer technique of ultrasonography appears to be safer, does not have the radiation hazard, and in skilled hands can demonstrate a number of fetal abnormalities. It is extremely valuable in localisation of the placenta and in the diagnosis of twins and multiple pregnancies. It seems likely that further advances in this technique will be of even more help in the early stages of pregnancy.

Fetoscopy is the most direct of all means of looking at the fetus but

1.   Carrier Detection - Parents

2.   Maternal Blood   - AFP

3.   Amniocentesis — Cytology
                   +
                   — Biochemistry

4.   Fetal Imaging — X-ray
                   — Ultrasound

5.   Direct Fetoscopy
      +

6.   Fetal Blood sampling

Table 7.1   Techniques employed in prenatal diagnosis. Carrier detection in parents is the first stage in recessive and sex-linked disease.

at present there are only a few centres in the country with experience of the procedure. The apparatus used is a fine fibre-optic telescope and there is still concern over the risks of introducing such an instrument into the uterus.

In most cases however, prenatal diagnosis implies amniocentesis and analysis of the liquor amnii. The technique is now a well established one, normally safe in experienced hands and said by some women not to be more upsetting than a visit to the dentist. However, this assessment is likely to vary according to the skill of the doctor and the dentist! Nevertheless, it is very important that before any woman undergoes this type of investigation, the risks are explained and that both she and her husband are fully aware of what is involved. Interference with a pregnancy should not be undertaken lightly and there should be good grounds for doing so. Most women find procedures of this sort during a pregnancy upsetting and it would be incorrect to assume that they are not anxious and frightened. Basically the procedure consists of transabdominal puncture of the uterus under local anaesthesia and the withdrawal of 5–10 mls of amniotic fluid. It is normally performed at approximately 14–16 weeks of gestation by which time the uterus is an abdominal as opposed to a pelvic organ and it is usually possible to manage the procedure on an out-patient basis. It is important to know the stage of gestation accurately and for this reason women should be encouraged to keep an accurate record of their period dates. Amniocentesis is less successful at 12 weeks and becomes easier with increasing gestation. Nevertheless, it should not be left too late because of the time necessary to prepare a fetal karyotype. This normally takes as long as three weeks and if amniocentesis has been delayed then the termination of the pregnancy, if it is requested, may present some difficulties.

There have been a number of studies on the hazards of amniocentesis. One of the more recent from Great Britain lists the following complications:

1. an increased risk of spontaneous abortion
2. some increase in the risk of ante-partum haemorrhage
3. some increased risk of respiratory problems in the infant at birth
4. increased risk of postural deformities in the fetus, e.g. talipes equino-varus and congenital dislocation of the hip. Increased evidence of pressure abnormalities, e.g. deformity of the skull and flattening of the nose and ears.
5. increased risk of rhesus iso-immunisation
6. increased risk of purulent chorionitis
7. some increase in the overall perinatal mortality

The risk of termination of a pregnancy is estimated at approximately 1 in 100 to 1 in 75. Some American reports have suggested a lower risk than this and it is important to remember that spontaneous abortion may occur at this stage of a pregnancy without interference. Nevertheless, the risk of the abnormality anticipated should be greater than that of a spontaneous termination. In most cases this will always be so but in the circumstances where amniocentesis is done primarily for maternal anxiety the risk of an abnormality may not be greater than that of the procedure. There does not appear to be any satisfactory explanation for the slight increase in ante-partum haemorrhage although rupture of the uterine wall blood vessel is a possibility. The fetal respiratory and orthopaedic problems could theoretically result from reduction in the amniotic fluid surrounding the infant, as could the pressure deformities. Mothers need to be informed that in approximately 5 per cent or 1 in 20 of patients repeat amniocentesis is necessary. If this point is made in the preliminary discussions there is not so much anxiety produced by the need for a further puncture. In some centres the mother or even father have to sign a consent form. This is not routine throughout Great Britain but would seem a sensible precaution and might at least give a guarantee that there had been some sort of explanation given. There is still need for improvements in the detailed management of patients having amniocentesis and this may make it possible to reduce complications further. Most reports stress the importance of ultrasonography as an aid to amniocentesis and there seems to be good evidence that the complications of the procedure are lessened by ultrasound localisation of the placenta and fetal position. Much of the emotional upset associated with amniocentesis could be

Neuro -Ectodermal Defects

Chromosomal Disorders

Sex-Linked Disorders

Biochemical Diseases

Miscellaneous Abnormalities

Table 7.2   Indications for prenatal diagnosis.

lessened by more emphasis on the details of patient management. There are good grounds for suggesting that a special team should be responsible for this type of work. Such a team would consist of an obstetrician, a midwife and secretarial staff. The genetic counselling service would obviously be involved in many situations and the combined services should help to minimise some current problems.

The indications for prenatal diagnosis are increasing but the main groups of conditions in which it is currently used and of value are seen in Table 7.2.

Neural Tube Defects

Biochemical studies of liquor amnii have been possible for many years and measurement of bilirubin pigment in the management of rhesus haemolytic disease is a well established technique. It has also been valuable in other situations, for example, assessment of fetal well-being late in pregnancy. However, a major advance occurred in 1972 when Brock and his colleages from Edinburgh reported that measurement of liquor alphafetoprotein could be used as a reliable means of detecting neural tube defects in the fetus in early pregnancy. This substance, a primitive protein, is present in fetal serum but virtually disappears from the circulation in the first few months after birth. Normally it is retained within the developing fetus but when there is a breach of fetal skin surface as in meningomyelocele or anencephaly, alphafetoprotein diffusion into the maternal liquor is increased and the increased level can be detected. The significant feature about this test is that it can be performed sufficiently early in pregnancy to allow for termination if the fetus is affected. Initially liquor alphafetoprotein was only measured in those pregnancies where there had been a previously affected infant. However, there was an obvious need for a screening test in all pregnancies if the incidence of the disease was to be significantly reduced. It was subsequently confirmed that there is an increase in maternal serum alphafetoprotein when the fetus is affected and estimation of serum

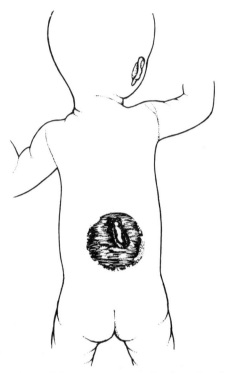

Fig. 7.2   Baby with large meningomyelocele and early hydro-cephalus. This large open lesion would almost certainly cause an elevation in liquor a-fetoprotein.

levels is now routine in most centres. It is, unfortunately, less reliable than examination of the liquor but there is no doubt that such a screening test is helping to reduce the incidence of this common disease. Although prenatal diagnosis offers undoubted benefits to many families, it is not too unexpected that problems do occur. It is now recognised that there are several conditions in addition to the neural tube abnormalities which will produce a rise in the serum and liquor alphafetoprotein. These are as follows:

1. multiple pregnancies (these should be diagnosed if ultrasound is used routinely)
2. fetal death or missed abortion
3. exomphalos and gastroschisis
4. Meckel's Syndrome (encephalocele, polydactyly and polycystic kidneys)

5. congenital nephrotic syndrome
6. sacrococcygeal teratoma
7. fetal scalp defects
8. ectopia vesica
9. Turner's Syndrome

In addition there have been several reports of raised levels in conditions other than those listed, e.g. high intestinal obstruction in the fetus and maternal hepatic carcinoma. Exomphalos and gastroschisis have a frequency of 1 in 2000 to 1 in 3000 births but Meckel's Syndrome, sacrococcygeal teratoma and the congenital nephrotic syndrome are all rare. In the vast majority of cases a positive result will indicate the presence of a neural tube defect and false positive results will be found in only approximately 1 in 500 to 1 in 1000 cases. Nearly all the fetal abnormalities which can produce false positive results are serious and termination of the pregnancy may not necessarily be a catastrophe. In many cases the false positive result is due to twins and it is important to exclude multiple pregnancy whenever a raised alphafetoprotein is found.

Anencephaly normally causes the higher levels of alphafetoprotein and is reliably diagnosed by ultrasound if there is any doubt. The majority of spinal lesions are of the open variety and these will also normally show a raised alphafetoprotein. However, a small percentage of meningomyeloceles, probably about 5 per cent, may be covered by skin and the alphafetoprotein level may not be raised. Fortunately, this type of lesion may be amenable to surgery. In general, in centres with experience it should be possible to detect between 75–80 per cent of serious neural tube defects. The most common reason for a false negative is an incorrect estimation of the length of gestation. If this is over-estimated the result may be abnormally low. It would not be appropriate to give parents lists of all the false positives and false negatives but they need to be aware of the limitations of the investigation. It is also important not to declare the fetus free of abnormality without a full post-mortem examination. When a termination has been performed because of a suspected neural tube defect and the baby at delivery has a normal looking spine this does not mean that there may not be some other abnormality. The kidneys and the alimentary tract need to be carefully examined and full post-mortem examination should be performed.

Chromosomal Abnormalities

The liquor contains cells from fetal skin and from the buccal mucosa. These cells can be obtained from the amniotic fluid and after culture a karyotype is prepared in the same way as from blood or other tissues. It should then be possible to detect changes in the total number of chromosomes as, for example, in the trisomies or monosomies; loss or deletion of part of a chromosome; or translocation of genetic material from one chromosome to another. In addition it is possible to determine fetal sex, the presence of two X chromosomes indicating the female and an X and Y chromosome, a male. The situations in which cytogenetics studies of the fetal cells are useful are:

1. Advanced maternal age. In mothers of 36 years or over there is an increased risk of Down's Syndrome, other autosomal trisomies and some sex chromosomal anomalies. Down's Syndrome with a frequency of 1.5/1000 live births is the most common. This condition is more common with advancing maternal age. One possible explanation for this is that non-disjunction of chromosomes at meiosis occurs more frequently in the older woman but the underlying explanation for this phenomenon is still not clear. At the age of 18 a woman's risk of having a child with Down's Syndrome is less than 1 in 2000, by the age of 30 it is probably about 1 in 300 and at the age of 45 and over is about 1 in 40. This increasing risk can be seen in Fig. 7.3. Childbearing is obviously commoner in younger women and, therefore, the majority of babies with this syndrome will continue to be born in this group. Women over the age of 40 give birth to only about 1 per cent of all live births and 50 per cent of children with Down's Syndrome are born to women under the age of 30. There has been a decrease in the number of children born to older women and although amniocentesis and cytogenetic studies are indicated in this group the total reduction in the number of children born with Down's Syndrome will be small. Nevertheless, it is considered worthwhile preventing the birth of babies with this condition where possible.

2. Mothers who have a previous child with trisomy 21. The recurrence risk to a couple who have already had an affected child depends on mother's age. Under 30 years the risk although increased is probably not much greater than 1 in 100. In the older woman the risk is appropriate to that for her age and is probably not much increased beyond this. Nevertheless, mothers who have had a baby with this condition normally request or are offered amniocentesis and it is unusual for this offer to be refused. In the younger woman with a low recurrence risk amniocentesis is, therefore, normally performed because of maternal anxiety. It is important to remember that the risk of another affected child is probably not much greater in this group of women than the risk of a spontaneous miscarriage as a result of the procedure. Nevertheless, maternal anxiety about a

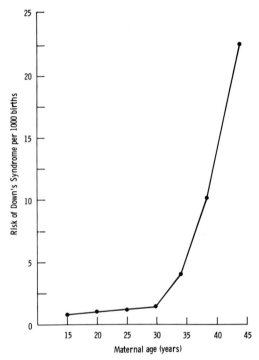

Fig. 7.3 Marked increase in risk of Down's Syndrome with increasing maternal age, particularly after 40.

pregnancy may be considerable and amniocentesis is probably justified. Some particular groups of women, those who look after children, doctors' wives and nurses may be very keen to have the reassurance such a test can offer. In these cases it may be that there are grounds for amniocentesis even when there has been no previously affected infant. Relatives of couples who have had a child with Down's Syndrome may also be very sensitive to the problems this brings and may request amniocentesis. Although probably not at increased risk the matter needs to be discussed. In certain circumstances therefore the obstetrician may consider maternal anxiety is sufficiently great to warrant the procedure. In every situation in which the risk of an affected infant is not increased it is important to remind the parents that all medical interference carries certain dangers and should not be undertaken lightly.

3. Translocation carriers. The majority of children with Down's Syndrome have trisomy 21. About 6–8 per cent, however, have the disease as a result of a translocation. In this situation, an extra No.

21 chromosome is translocated onto another chromosome, usually in the group 13–15. When this abnormality is present in a child it is normally shown that mother or, less commonly, father, is a translocation carrier. Unlike the child they have only two No. 21 chromosomes but one of these is translocated onto another chromosome. Because they have not lost or gained any genetic information the translocation is said to be balanced in the carrier. In the child with three No. 21s the translocation is said to be unbalanced. When mother carries the translocation the risk of an affected offspring is very high, 1 in 8 to 1 in 10. When father is the carrier, however, the risk tends to be much lower, probably nearer 1 in 20.

It has now become common practice to investigate the chromosomes of any woman with a history of recurrent miscarriages. Approximately 10 per cent of such women may be shown to have a balanced translocation and if they become pregnant then the risks are the same as those quoted above. It is equally important in this situation, however, to examine the karyotype of this woman's mother and father. If either are found to have a balanced translocation then all their children must be examined as all are at risk of having the same carrier state. Fig. 7.4 is of such a family. Mrs S. had a miscarriage and on examination was shown to have a balanced translocation between chromosomes No. 13 and 15. This prompted examination of her son who was found to have normal chromosomes. Mother's mother, however, was also a carrier as were five of her sibs. Their families in turn will have to be examined and those found to have an abnormality advised accordingly. Another source

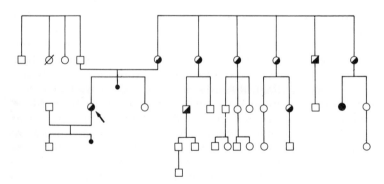

Fig. 7.4   Pedigree of family with 13·15 translocation. Mother (arrow) requested karyotype although she had only one definite miscarriage. Very much to everyone's surprise she was found to have a translocation. A vast amount of work for the counselling staff locating and karyotyping other family members.

of translocation carriers is the male infertility clinic and a proportion of males with infertility can be shown to have a translocation of the balanced type. The exact relationship of this abnormality to their infertility is not known. Their families and sibs also need to be investigated and when carriers are found amniocentesis offered to them at the appropriate time. Carriers of balanced translocations between any other chromosomes should also be offered amniocentesis. In general it can be stated that an unbalanced translocation is very likely to produce severe physical abnormalities and mental subnormality in the affected person. Theoretically one could expect to have translocations occurring between any of the chromosomes. It is not known why translocations between No. 21 and group 13–15 are more common. It may be that chromosomes No. 21 and others with unequal arms, the so-called acrocentric chromosomes have more potential breakage points along their length. On occasions a translocation occurs in a child with normal parents and there has been no hereditary transmission. This type of translocation is said to have occurred *de novo*.

4.   X chromosomal abnormality. Amniocentesis is usually also offered to a woman who has had a child with a sex *chromosomal abnormality*, e.g. Turner's Syndrome or Klinefelter's Syndrome. The recurrence risk of a similar abnormality is low but maternal anxiety may be high. It can be difficult to know what to advise if one of these two common sex chromosomal anomalies is found unexpectedly on amniocentesis. This is likely to be a recurrent problem with increasing availability of this test in pregnancy. Most girls with Turner's Syndrome are dwarfed; they may have an increased risk of intellectual retardation and 25 per cent have congenital heart lesions. These facts have to be explained clearly and the decision about termination should always be made by the couple concerned. The boy with Klinefelter's Syndrome is infertile and has a risk of intellectual retardation. Some mothers might wish to terminate a pregnancy with this information. The fetus with an XYY karyotype presents even more of a problem. These children may look perfectly normal and all that one can say is that they may have an increased incidence of psychiatric illness and possibly an increased tendency to antisocial behaviour culminating in brushes with the law. This might be considered inadequate grounds for termination of a pregnancy. The matter needs to be frankly discussed with the parents and their decision concerning the pregnancy must be respected.

5. If either parent has mosaicism, that is two or more different karyotypes, then there is a risk of an abnormal fetus and amniocentesis is indicated. Mosaicism of the sex chromosomes is commoner than of the autosomes but mosaics for trisomy 21 are well documented. Mosaicism is not uncommon and may occur if there is non-disjunction early in embryogenesis. Two chromosomally distinct cell lines may then develop and continue to multiply. This has very different consequences from non-disjunction occurring during gametogenesis, when one abnormal cell line is produced and only this one survives. If the mosaicism affects the sex chromosomes then an individual may have two cell lines, for example, one with karyotype X0 and another with karyotype XX. This is written X0/XX, the diagonal representing mosaicism. If the autosomes are affected then one cell line will have a different constitution from another. Such an abnormality constitutes about 2 per cent of the total chromosomal abnormalities found in Down's Syndrome. Such individuals have a 46,XY/47,XY+21, karyotype if male and a 46,XX/47,XX+21, if female. When a child is born with this abnormality the risk to subsequent offspring is about the same as if it had been the result of regular trisomy 21. Mosaicism for other autosomes including No. 8 have been described and the same risk is probably applicable. Other patients with sex chromosomal mosaicism may have some cells with a 46,XY, constitution and other with 47,XXY. This is written 46,XY/47,XXY, and such patients may demonstrate

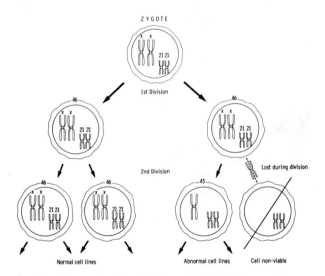

Fig. 7.5   One method by which mosaicism of the sex chromosomes may arise. There are two cell lines. One normal with XX constitution. The abnormal cell line has an X0 constitution (only two pairs of chromosomes in diagram). Mosaicism may also occur if the zygote commences with an X0 constitution.

all the features of Klinefelter's Syndrome. The percentage of cells with the abnormal karyotype does not always seem to bear a definite relationship to the degree of clinical abnormality.

6. It can be difficult in some cases to be sure of the significance of some chromosomal anomalies. For example, in an otherwise normal adult a karyotype may reveal an extra piece of chromosomal material referred to as a marker chromosome. It is impossible to state definitely whether this may or may not have significance for a pregnancy. The size of the marker chromosome and its origin are important factors. In such situations a decision should be made only after full discussion with the parents. Occasionally a similar abnormality of the fetal karyotype is found when there was another indication for amniocentesis such as a neural tube anomaly. As in the previous situation discussion with the parents and obstetrician is essential. If mother or father is shown to have a similar abnormality but is normal physically and intellectually, then obviously reassurance can be given. If no such abnormality is present in them the parents may have to be told that the outcome of the pregnancy is

Reason for Referral	Tested	Chromosome Abnormalities Found
A. Primarily because CNS defect suspected		
History of CNS defect in family	285	1
Raised serum α - F protein	653	5
B. Primarily because chromosome abnormality may be present		
Age 35 - 39	585	9
Age 40 and over	176	8
History of chromosome abn. in family	131	2
Previous cong. malformed child	45	1
Previous history of abortion / miscarriage	10	0
Maternal anxiety	33	0
Other reasons	82	0
total	2,000	26
		(1.3%)

Table 7.3 Chromosomal abnormalities in first 2000 individuals tested. Although the number detected seems small it is cost-effective, i.e. the expense incurred identifying the abnormal fetus is less than the cost of looking after affected individuals. Of greater importance is the benefit to the individual families.

Abnormal Karyotypes In First 2,000 Samples

Numerical Abnormalities	number	Structural Abnormalities	number
47, XX, +21	3	(A) Balanced Karyotypes	
47, XY, +21	4	46, XX, t (7. 11)	1
47, XX, +18	2	46, XY, t (19. 20)	1
47, XY, +18	2	46, XX, t (13. 16)	1
46, XX /47, XX, +22	1	46, XY, t (13. 14)	1
46, XX /47, XX, +21	1	46, XX, t (10. 11)	1
47, XYY	1	(B) Unbalanced Karyotypes	
47, XXX	1	46, XX, 15p +	1
45, XO	1	46, XY, 12q +	1
46, XX /45, XO	1	46, XY, - 14, t (14q 21q) mat	1
47, XY, + marker	1		

Total abnormal karyotypes = 26   Mean number of days to reporting = 18

Table 7.4   The type of chromosomal abnormality detected in fetal cells obtained by amniocentesis (mat. is abbreviation for maternal, mother carried balanced translocation). The pregnancies with the balanced translocation went to term. Those with unbalanced translocations were terminated.

unknown. This is obviously unsatisfactory but the counsellor's role is to inform and to help the parents come to a decision. It should normally not be to tell them what to do.

X-linked diseases

When a woman is known to be a carrier of an X-linked disease such as Duchenne muscular dystrophy or haemophilia then any male infant born to her has a 50/50 chance of being affected by the disease and any daughter a 50/50 chance of being a carrier like her mother. In various centres it has been the practice to determine the sex of the fetus and if this is male to offer a termination of the pregnancy. In this way only females are carried to term and they should not have any manifestations of the disease. This procedure, however, is far from ideal. There is a 50/50 chance that a male fetus may be normal and any daughter has the same risk of being a carrier with the same subsequent difficult decision to make about her own children. Obviously it would be more satisfactory to demonstrate that a male fetus suffered from the disease. This has become possible recently as a result of advances in fetoscopy. Using this instrument it is possible to identify fetal blood vessels and a specimen of fetal blood can be obtained. The serum creatine kinase is normally grossly elevated in patients with Duchenne muscular dystrophy and has been shown to be elevated early in fetal life in the few patients examined. However, it has been recently recognised that the creatine kinase level may be considerably raised in the normal fetus and this may make interpretation of the results difficult. In addition it is important that the parents are made aware that fetoscopy carries considerable risk, 4–8 per cent, of producing a miscarriage.

Metabolic Disorders

The inherited metabolic disorders are an important group of genetic diseases with wide variation in clinical severity. Some produce little upset but others are extremely serious and may be associated with mental retardation and a high mortality. Phenylketonuria is one of the more common conditions with a frequency of approximately 1 in 10 000 births. Some others have a frequency of less than 1 in 40 000. Overall, however, the combined incidence may be as high as 1 in 100 live births.

The majority are inherited as autosomal recessive traits and as a rule the carrier state of the parents is only recognised following the birth of an affected infant. The recurrence risk is therefore high, 25 per cent, and with serious disorders many parents have welcomed help from prenatal diagnosis. This has become possible as a result of advances in our understanding of the underlying biochemical disturbance and the demonstration of the specific defect. It has also been dependent on improvements in cell culture technique and the ability to identify enzyme deficiencies in cultured fetal fibroblasts. Although over 50 of these biochemical disorders have been diagnosed prenatally, in some instances only one or two families have been involved. In practice, therefore, there is only a small number of well documented conditions which can be confidently and reliably diagnosed *in utero*. These are listed in Table 7.5.

Tay-Sachs Disease is an example of a group of diseases referred to as the sphingolipidoses. Other diseases in this group are Gaucher's Disease, metachromatic leucodystrophy and Krabbe's leucodystrophy. In Tay-Sachs Disease there is a deficiency of the enzyme, hexosaminidase-A, and all the manifestations of the disease result from lack of this substance. The condition is more common in the Ashkenazi Jewish population and affected children show failure to thrive, mental retardation and various neurological manifestations. They normally die at the age of 3–4 years. The enzyme deficiency can be demonstrated in fetal cells obtained by amniocentesis and subsequently cultured. In this disease there is also a deficiency of hexosaminidase-A in human serum and it is usually possible,

Disorder	Enzyme Deficiency
Sphingolipidoses	
Tay - Sachs Disease	Hexoseaminadase - A
Gauchers Disease	Glucocerebrosidase
Metachromatic Leucodystrophy	Arylsulphatase
Krabbes Leucodystrophy	Galactocerbroside - β - Galactosidase
Pompes Disease (glycogen storage)	α - I - 4 - Glucosidase
Mucopolysaccharidoses	
Hurler Disease	α - L - Iduronidase
Hunter Disease	Sulpho - Iduronide Sulphatase
Sanfilippo Disease	Heparan Sulphate Sulphatase
Galactosaemia	Galactose - I - Phosphate Uridyl Transferase
Homocystinuria	Cystathionine Synthetase
Maple Syrup Urine Disease	Keto Acid Decarboxylase
Methylmalonic Acidaemia	Methylmalonic CoA Mutase

Table 7.5   Inherited metabolic disorders. In practice these are the most commonly diagnosed conditions.

therefore, to detect the heteroxygous 'carrier' state in individuals. This is important in certain high risk groups such as Ashkenazic Jews in whom the incidence of the disease is approximately 1 in 6000. This means that one person in 40 is heterozygous for the gene. Such populations can be screened and couples found to be 'carriers' can be offered counselling and prenatal diagnosis.

In Gaucher's Disease there is enlargement of the liver and spleen associated with neurological abnormalities. The majority of patients die before the age of three and only a few survive to late childhood or adult life. As with many other metabolic disturbances there are several different forms of the disease with varying clinical presentation. The basic biochemical abnormality is deficiency of the enzyme glucocerebrosidase.

Pompe's Disease is one of ten glycogen storage disorders and results from a deficiency of the enzyme, α-glucosidase. This results in the accumulation of glycogen in various organs and is usually fatal early in life. Meantime only a few of the glycogen storage diseases can be diagnosed prenatally.

The mucopolysaccharidoses are of three main types; Hurler, Hunter and Sanfilippo Syndromes. Demonstration of the specific enzyme deficiency in these conditions is possible by the incorporation of radio-active sulphate into cultured amniotic fluid cells. All three diseases are associated with progressive neurological deterioration and striking physical abnormalities. The patient with Hurler's Syndrome has coarse features, is usually dwarfed and has corneal opacities. Excessive amounts of mucopolysaccharides can be demonstrated in the urine. In Sanfilippo's Syndrome the patients are similar to those with Hurler's Syndrome. Hunter's disease is also recessively inherited but is X-linked. Clinically the patients, all males, resemble the other two.

In galactosaemia, affected children fail to thrive, develop cataracts, mental retardation and cirrhosis. The disease may respond to restriction of lactose at birth. However, it is not possible to forecast the outcome of such treatment in all cases and this point has to be explained to the parents. Homocystinuria is usually associated with severe mental retardation, dislocated lenses and abnormalities of the limbs resembling Marfan's Syndrome or arachnodactyly. The disorder is due to a deficiency of cystathionine synthetase which can be demonstrated in cultured cells from fetal skin.

Prenatal diagnosis of all these conditions requires considerable expertise. For this reason it is normally recommended that only a few laboratories in the United Kingdom should be responsible for this type of work. This would give the best guarantee of reliability of the results and in all forms of prenatal diagnosis this is an extremely important factor. A list of such laboratories is available in all genetic centres.

Further advances in fetoscopy and ultrasound are almost inevitable. A safe and reliable means of direct examination of the fetus would help in the diagnosis of single gene conditions with a high recurrence risk and a few such conditions are listed in Table 7.6. In practice it is not always easy to be sure of the fetal abnormality and

Fetoscopy (± Ultrasonography)

Disorder	Abnormalities Potentially Visible
Anophthalmos (A. R.)	Absent Eyes
Ellis-van Crevald (A. R.)	Abnormality of Hands (polydactyl; reduction deformities)
Holt-Oram (A. D.)	Reduction Deformity (radial ray) upper limbs
Roberts Syndrome (A. R.)	Reduction Deformity All Limbs (phocomelia) + hare lip
Peromelia (A. R.)	Reduction Deformity Upper Limbs
Meckel Syndrome (A. R.)	Polydactyly + Encephalocele

Table 7.6   Some conditions which are potentially diagnosable at fetoscopy. (A.R. – recessive A.D. – dominant.)

fetoscopy still does carry a considerable risk to the pregnancy. Ultrasound is currently of value in the diagnosis of twins and multiple pregnancies. It is also extremely helpful in localising the placenta prior to amniocentesis. Several studies have confirmed that this reduces the number of failed taps and the risk of bleeding into the liquor. The use of this technique will undoubtedly increase and in expert hands may be of value in the diagnosis of conditions such as hydrocephalus or microcephaly. It can also be helpful in the prenatal diagnosis of renal cystic disease in the fetus. This may be suspected if either parent has cystic kidney disease and in the dominantly inherited variety the risk to offspring will be 50/50. Congenital abnormalities of the renal tract are common and both cystic disease and renal agenesis may be seen in Potter's Syndrome. Babies with this condition have a peculiar facies, spade-like hands and frequently bilateral talipes equinovarus. They die very soon after delivery from

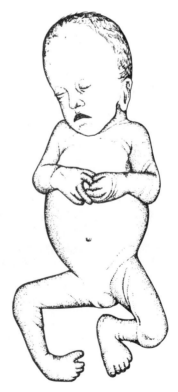

Fig. 7.6   Potter's Syndrome. These babies die soon after birth.

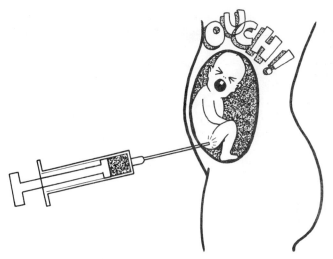

Fig. 7.7   Prenatal diagnosis!

increasing respiratory failure due to pulmonary hypoplasia. All these features are the result of oligohydramnios. Renal agenesis appears to be of a multifactorial origin and the recurrence risk may be 1 : 25.

Prenatal diagnosis will continue to present problems for both parents and staff involved in the procedure. Ideally the diagnosis of any of the conditions discussed should be reliable and safe. There is an obvious need for continuing research. The parents' consent should be obtained only after discussion of the full significance of the investigation. It is important to remember that most women find this type of interference upsetting and waiting for the test results can be very trying. If the results indicate an affected fetus then termination of the pregnancy should be as expeditious as possible and follow-up of the parents is essential. The desire to have a normal baby is common to most parents; their involvement in prenatal testing should make everyone concerned very sympathetic to their predicament.

8
Special
Problems

Many of the conditions which have been discussed so far will be met by nurses and doctors in the major specialities but there are some problems with considerable genetic implications which occur in specialist fields. It would be impossible to deal with all of these in detail and where there is any doubt about the genetic aspects of a particular condition the nurse should consult a more comprehensive text. (See recommended reading.) However, some specialist areas do have common problems, e.g. children or adults with blindness or deafness may be seen initially by the paediatric nursing staff and then subsequently become the responsibility of the specialist ophthalmic nurse or school nurse. Patients with mental retardation will normally be recognised initially in the paediatric or obstetric departments but subsequently will be cared for by the specialist nurse with training in the management of mental retardation. These specialised nursing areas are likely to contain a considerable number of patients whose disabilities have resulted from genetic factors. For this and other reasons it seems likely that there will be an increasing demand for genetic counselling for the patients and families in these various groups.

1. The nurse and mental retardation

It is difficult to assess the true incidence of mental retardation in a community, but between 3–6 per cent of the general population have IQs below 50, i.e. are severely retarded. Some of these patients have very obvious associated physical abnormalities which can help in the diagnosis, e.g. Down's Syndrome. Other, however, have only minimal physical problems and their mental retardation is said to be non-specific. This may or may not be of genetic origin. All such individuals require intensive initial investigation to exclude potentially treatable diseases such as phenylketonuria. It seems likely that a number of diseases are awaiting recognition and the nurse and doctor working in this difficult field should find it very stimulating.

As in other situations a thorough pedigree is necessary and this usually means the inclusion of at least three generations. The history of the pregnancy including drug ingestion, details of the perinatal period and medical and social factors are all important. Any child with a combination of mental retardation and physical defects warrants chromosomal analysis. This also applies to easily recognised conditions such as Down's Syndrome. This will ensure that chromosomal anomalies such as translocations are not overlooked. The more thorough the investigation of retarded children the more likely it is that individuals may be placed in specific groups.

In Table 8.1 it can be seen that severe mental retardation may result from genetic factors in 30–50 per cent of children. There are various figures quoted in reports from different parts of the world. When this group is further analysed some types of retardation are seen to be the result of single gene defects and others associated with chromosomal abnormalities. The single gene defects comprise dominant, recessive and X-linked conditions and the genetic advice in such situations is usually straightforward.

It has always been appreciated that males outnumber females in institutions for the mentally retarded. This is now recognised to be due to the frequency of sex-linked disease in the retarded population. Fig. 8.1 is of a family with classical X-linked mental retardation. The affected males in this family had no very obvious associated physical abnormalities but two of them did have convulsions. The condition is referred to as Renpenning's Syndrome and its significance lies in the fact that the mother of the affected boys must be an obligatory carrier of the abnormal gene. This in turn implies that any of her daughters has a 1 in 2 risk of being a carrier and, therefore, has a risk of 1 in 8 of having a retarded son. This figure is arrived at as follows:

(a) each daughter has a 1 in 2 risk of being a carrier
(b) she has a 1 in 2 risk of having a son (approx.)
(c) each son has a 1 in 2 risk of being affected

The overall risk is therefore

$$\tfrac{1}{2} \times \tfrac{1}{2} \times \tfrac{1}{2} = \tfrac{1}{8}$$

Some males with this condition, although not having any very obvious physical defects, may have large testes; others do not have this

	Incidence (approx)
A. Genetic Factors	35%

Chromosomal
Downs Syndrome
Trisomy 18
Trisomy 13
Etc.

Single Gene
Tuberose Sclerosis (A. D.)
Metabolic Disorders
    Phenylketonuria (A. R.)
    Lesch - Nyhan Syndrome (X. L.)
    Hunters Disease (X. L.)
Renpennings Syndrome (X. L.)
Cornelia de Lange (A. R.)
Rubinstein - Taybi (A. R.)

Multifactorial
Hydrocephalus + Meningomyelocele
Others

B. Perinatal Factors	20%

Low Birth Wt.
    Prematurity
    Light for Dates
Asphyxia
Cerebral Haemorrhage
Infection

C. Post - Natal Factors	15%

Infections e. g. meningitis
                  encephalitis
Trauma... accidental
           non accidental
Psychoses
Others

D. Unknown	30%

A. D. autosomal dominant
A. R. autosomal recessive
X. L. X - linked

Table 8.1   Causes of mental retardation.

associated feature. Recently there has been considerable interest in reports of an abnormality of the X chromosome in this syndrome. The abnormality is not a gross one but can be demonstrated by

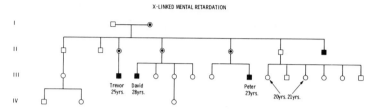

Fig. 8.1 Renpenning's Syndrome. The consultands were sisters who were soon to marry; one was nearly 20, the other nearly 22. Both were reassured. Since their father was normal he could not pass the responsible gene to either of them.

special techniques and consists of a constriction of the long arm of an X chromosome. When an affected male has this abnormality it might be possible to demonstrate a similar chromosomal anomaly in his carrier mother and also in any carrier sister. If this finding is confirmed it would make genetic counselling very much more accurate. It might eventually become possible to offer prenatal diagnosis by fetal karyotype examination.

There are a number of well documented syndromes with associated mental retardation which are dominantly inherited. Most of these have associated physical anomalies which can help in the diagnosis.

However, some conditions which are well recognised as being dominantly inherited may cause disease in a child born to two apparently normal parents. This is frequently the case with adenoma sebaceum, or tuberose sclerosis. As many as 80 per cent of patients with this condition have normal parents. Under these circumstances the disease is thought to have resulted from a new mutation. Increased paternal age is often a factor in such mutations but the reasons for this are unclear. The chance of a further similar mutation occurring in the same family is very small and most mutation rates are in the order of 10^{-5} or 1/100 000. However, occasionally more than one affected child can be born to apparently normal parents. In some cases this can be explained by assuming that one or other parent has gonadal mosaicism; the ova or sperm having a mixture of normal cells and abnormal cells containing the mutated gene. Such a mechanism is thought to explain recurrence in a number of conditions in which the parents are apparently clinically normal. It is very important, however, before assuming gonadal mosaicism to exclude even minor evidence of the disease in the parents. Because of the possibility of this type of inheritance a recurrence risk of 1 in 10 is quoted to normal parents who have had one child with this disease.

Recessively inherited conditions frequently produce a biochemical

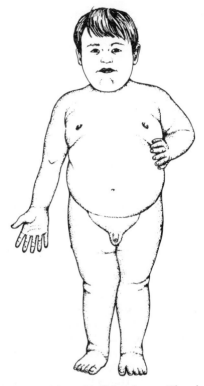

Fig. 8.2   Laurence-Moon-Biedl Syndrome. The obesity is very obvious. It is necessary to look more closely to spot the polydactyly!

abnormality which in turn produces mental retardation. In some of these the biochemical disorder may be demonstrable but in others it is impossible to demonstrate any specific defect. In the Laurence-Moon-Biedl Syndrome, the patients have polydactyly and older children are often obese. In addition they have hypogenitalism and many will show a typical retinal change, the so-called retinitis pigmentosa. Patients with Carpenter's Syndrome have a small head, premature fusion of the cranial sutures and the face shows a flat profile. There is syndactyly of the hands and usually polysyndactyly of the feet. In neither of these syndromes is there a demonstrable biochemical abnormality nor does it seem likely that a single chemical deficiency could produce such widespread changes.

Microcephaly associated with mental retardation may be transmitted in a recessive fashion. However, many retarded patients, irrespective of the cause, may have a head circumference below the normal range. On occasions it can be very difficult to distinguish between recessively inherited microcephaly, so called primary microcephaly, and microcephaly associated with other conditions, secondary microcephaly. A number of syndromes with retardation and microcephaly occur with a frequency suggestive of autosomal recessive inheritance. There is more than one affected child in the family and there may be consanguinity. Similar cases may be sporadic however and the recurrence risk in these two situations obviously will be different. In the Cornelia de Lange Syndrome the patients are microcephalic and have a characteristic facies with pronounced hirsutism and eyebrows which meet in the mid-line. This is referred to as synophrys and should not be taken as an invariable sign of mental retardation. Many successful people, even politicians, have such eyebrows! When one child is born with this syndrome the recurrence risk for subsequent pregnancies is about 1 in 50. This is an empiric risk which implies that it is computed by studying large numbers of affected families and estimating the number with more than one affected child. However, if two children have been born with the condition the recurrence risk should be assumed high, i.e. 1 in 4, and the inheritance pattern is likely to be recessive.

Many chromosomal abnormalities may be associated with intellectual retardation. Down's Syndrome is by far the most common, but there are others and most of the trisomic states are normally associated with disturbance of intellect. Most unbalanced translocations in addition to producing a variety of physical defects may also cause mental retardation. The balanced form, on the other hand, does not appear to affect brain development and the incidence of balanced translocations in the general population may be as high as 1 in 100.

On occasions it is possible to demonstrate a small marker chromosome in some children with physical abnormalities associated with mental subnormality. It may or may not be possible to decide the source of this small piece of material. It is important not to assume that it is the cause of the retardation in every case. As we have discussed previously, if a similar marker chromosome is found in a parent who is mentally and physically normal then this abnormality cannot be considered to be the cause of the child's problem.

A large number of children with mental retardation do not have genetic disease. Their condition may have resulted from a number of factors including anoxia in association with prematurity or severe anoxia from other causes. Obviously in these circumstances the recurrence risk for such an abnormality is low. A second affected child would be dependent on a similar event in another pregnancy. It is worth remembering, however, that it is not possible to give the parents in this situation absolute reassurance about the future. They still have a risk of having a child with mental retardation from other causes and this risk needs to be discussed. When there has been one child in whom the cause of the mental retardation is unknown the recurrence risk is usually about 1 in 20 to 1 in 30, a low risk. In this situation one of the essentials for accurate genetic counselling is missing, i.e. there is no firm diagnosis.

The burden of looking after a child with mental retardation is a very onerous one. Most of us would not see a risk of 1 in 20 to 1 in 30 as high, but many parents already coping with such a problem in their family might feel it was sufficiently high for them not to consider having further children. This would be less likely if a prenatal test was available in some of the recessively inherited diseases or chromosomal abnormalities. When the parents do decide not to have further children they must be referred for sound family planning advice. With increasing knowledge more and more causes of disturbance of brain function will be discovered and counselling will become more accurate.

Epilepsy is frequently associated with mental retardation or may occur as an isolated finding. When it is part of a syndrome then the recurrence risk will be appropriate to that particular condition. In many instances, however, the cause of the mental retardation may be unknown and epilepsy is a complicating factor. Because there is a higher proportion of mentally retarded males than females, the risk may have to vary according to the sex of the affected child. Overall, however, the recurrence risk for another child with retardation associated with epilepsy is about 1 in 20. Patients suffering from epilepsy but without mental retardation or other physical abnormalities are often referred for genetic counselling. This is an important problem and produces anxiety out of proportion to the risk involved. There are various types of epilepsy and it is important to establish the exact type where possible. It is also helpful to have an EEG and detailed pedigree information. Recurrence risks will depend on all these factors but in general the risk to offspring of an affected individual may be between 1 in 20 and 1 in 30. It is likely to be higher if both parents are affected.

The nurse responsible for the management of children and adults with mental retardation is not usually involved with isolated psychiatric illness. However, disturbed emotional behaviour is common and some of these conditions have genetic implications. Schizophrenia appears to have a strong genetic component but this does not seem to be unifactorial. Risk estimates are, therefore, empiric, and as with many other conditions a firm diagnosis is essential. In some patients this may be straightforward but in others there may be considerable difficulty. In all psychiatric illness there is need for guidance from an experienced psychiatrist and genetic counselling should rarely be given without his advice. When a patient has been affected by schizophrenia the risk to the offspring is probably about 1 in 10 but is much higher if both parents are affected. Where group therapy is used in treatment of this disease the possibility of affected persons meeting and marrying cannot be ignored. This applies in other situations also and deaf people not infrequently choose a spouse with a hearing deficiency.

2. The school nurse and the handicapped school leaver

Young people attending special schools for the physically handicapped suffer from a wide variety of conditions many of which have a genetic aetiology. Children are normally referred to such centres from a wide geographical area and some of the families may not have received genetic counselling. This may be no longer relevant if mother is past the reproductive years but may be very helpful to the young person about to leave school. When this type of advice is offered it is important to have the co-operation of the community health services, headmistresses and matrons of the schools concerned.

Table 8.2 lists the type of diseases likely to be encountered. Many of the children suffer from spina bifida and the majority of them will be seriously handicapped. Those with average intelligence are more likely to understand and benefit from the advice offered. Some will suffer from muscular dystrophy but young people with Duchenne muscular dystrophy are not counselled in view of the prognosis for this disease. Before the first attendance the parents are given an explanation about the service and the problems which will be discussed. Few have so far refused the offer of counselling and at the first interview parents and pupils attend together. In this way it is possible to obtain reliable family pedigree information and to assess parental intelligence and the young person's family relationships. If the parents happen to be still in the childbearing age, they can be given recurrence risks and genetic counselling in the usual way. Subsequently the school leavers are seen on their own and it is then possible to discuss risks and matters relating to childbirth and marriage more openly. There seems to be no doubt that the majority benefit from such a discussion. The parents usually welcome this additional information and in many cases the genetic aspects have not been discussed previously. It has been instructive to learn that

Neural Tube Abnormalities	12
Spinabifida c̄ meningocele	
Spinabifida c̄ meningomyelocele	
Hydrocephalus	
Fragilitas Osseum (A.D.)	6
Congenital Abnormalities hands and feet	4
Congenital Cataracts (A.D.)	2
Muscular Dystrophy (non - Duchenne)	5
Peroneal Muscular Atrophy (A.D.)	
Limb Girdle (A.R.)	
Faccoscapulohumeral (A.D.)	
Sacral Teratoma	2
	31

Table 8.2   Referrals from special schools. 'The handicapped school leaver'.

following the introduction of this type of service the pupils have been more anxious to discuss related issues with the school matron or nurse. Initial reports suggest that genetic counselling to this group is useful and welcome, but further experience is necessary.

Patients affected by spina bifida with paralysed legs, bladder and rectal troubles may still be capable of having children. The risk to their offspring can be assessed by using the affected school-leaver as the index case and quoting a risk similar to that quoted to normal parents whose first child is affected, i.e. approximately 1 in 20. This is not a high risk but leads naturally to a discussion about amniocentesis and its benefits. There have now been a number of reports on girls with spina bifida who have had normal children and in one instance at least a normal child has been born to parents both of whom have had this condition. In the muscular dystrophies and bone diseases the risk to the affected person's children is assessed in the same way as for any other genetic problem and the same principles hold good. It is important to have an exact diagnosis and adequate pedigree information. The risk and other advice must then be conveyed with tact and sensitivity bearing in mind the age of the counsellees. As might have been anticipated many young girls of 16 or 17 are already sufficiently mature to appreciate and benefit from genetic advice. However, further experience will be necessary to decide the best means of giving this type of information to boys of the same age. They are usually more immature than girls and their

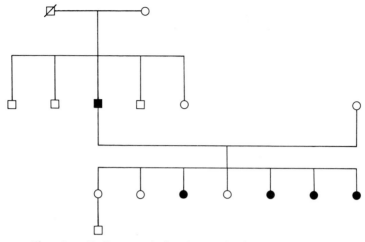

Fig. 8.3 Pedigree of family with fragilitas osseum (osteogenesis imperfecta). Two of the daughters attended a school for the physically handicapped. Both visited the genetic counselling clinic. In this family the inheritance is dominant.

approach to handicap and the future may be very different. In those cases where the physical handicap is obviously not of genetic origin considerable reassurance can be given about the future. This may be particularly helpful to a young person who has been harbouring real fears about the risk to offspring and the possible effects on a marriage.

3. The ophthalmic nurse

A number of diseases affecting the eyes have a very obvious genetic basis and in several surveys about 50 per cent of all children attending schools for the blind suffered from genetic diseases.

Gross microphthalmia and on occasions, anophthalmia, complete absence of the eye, may be recessively inherited with the usual 1 in 4 risk of a subsequent affected sibling. Obviously if there was some similar defect in a parent this would make the condition much more likely to be dominantly inherited. As we have seen in all genetic counselling work it is important to examine the parents and to take a proper family pedigree. A number of chromosomal abnormalities including classical Down's Syndrome may be associated with abnormalities of the eyes such as cataract and squint. Retinoblastoma, when bilateral, is a well recognised dominantly inherited tumour and with one or other parent affected the risk to offspring is

Genetic Factors	Incidence (approx) 50 % (in childhood)
Single Gene	
Autosomal Dominant	Bilateral Retinoblastoma Cataracts Macular Dystrophy Atypical Retinitis Pigmentosa Choroidal Sclerosis Doynes Choroiditis
Autosomal Recessive	Retinitis Pigmentosa Retinal Aplasia Amaurotic Idiocy Macular Dystrophy Sjögren – Larsson Syndrome Choroidal Sclerosis
X –Linked	Retinitis Pigmentosa Optic Atrophy Norries Disease Pseudoglioma
Environmental Factors	50 % (in childhood)
	Optic Atrophy Diabetes Accidents Retrolental Fibroplasia Uveitis Cataracts Others

Table 8.3   Causes of blindness. The incidence of various types of blindness varies according to age. In childhood genetic factors account for 50 per cent of all cases, but in middle and late life this figure is very much less.

50/50 of having the same condition. Although in many cases this tumour is treatable in terms of saving life, in others secondary deposits may occur in other tissues and the patients succumb. When the parent has unilateral retinoblastoma the risk to offspring is not as great and probably nearer 1 in 20.

Retinitis pigmentosa may appear as part of a more widespread syndrome, for example, the Laurence-Moon-Biedl Syndrome, or may be an isolated condition. Because of its peculiar onset there is a gradual restriction of the peripheral visual fields. For this reason it is

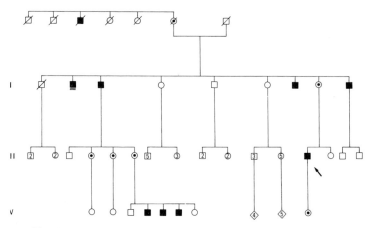

Fig. 8.4 Retinitis Pigmentosa. This disease shows different modes of inheritance (genetic heterogeneity). In this family the inheritance is X-linked. All affected males have carrier daughters. There is never male to male transmission.

referred to by the lay public as 'tunnel vision' and a number of lay societies have now sprung up to help sufferers from this disease. When present as a single gene disorder it may be inherited recessively or may be X-linked or even dominant. Skilled help from an ophthalmologist may be necessary to distinguish between these various groups. A properly constructed family pedigree may show vertical transmission affecting either sex and, therefore, dominant inheritance. It may occasionally demonstrate affected males only, no male to male transmission and this would suggest X-linked inheritance. In the absence of vertical transmission and with several affected sibs the disease may be considered recessively inherited. In the X-linked and recessive varieties it may be possible to show the heterozygote state in the female carriers; this obviously would have considerable benefit for counselling. It can be anticipated that more and more families with ophthalmic problems will be referred for genetic counselling advice in the future.

4. The nurse and deafness

Deafness, like blindness, may result from both genetic and environmental factors. Maternal rubella during pregnancy is one cause of deafness which has been recognised for some time. There have been suggestions that intrauterine infections with the cytomegalovirus may also damage the 8th nerve or the central brain receptors for

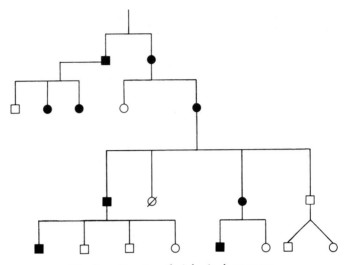

Fig. 8.5 Dominantly inherited cataracts.

sound. Some premature babies who have suffered severe perinatal anoxia may have impaired hearing in association with other abnormalities such as intellectual impairment. Deafness may also occur in the post-natal period as a result of meningitis, head injury or encephalitis. Local conditions in the ear such as chronic bilateral otitis media may also impair hearing to varying degrees. Hearing loss may be associated with congenital abnormalities of the ear which in turn may be associated with other physical defects comprising some well recognised syndromes and examples of these are listed in Table 8.4. As with so many of the problems we have discussed, diagnosis is an essential first step before advising about the future.

In Waardenburg's Syndrome deafness is associated with pigmentary disturbances and the condition is dominantly inherited. Affected patients show blond or grey forelocks or streaks in their hair. There may be different colours of the irides, so-called heterochromia irides. It is very important, therefore, to thoroughly examine any deaf person for evidence of pigmentary changes and the extent of these will vary within a family. As with all dominantly inherited diseases some patients may have the full blown syndrome whereas others may show only partial manifestations. In the Treacher-Collins Syndrome the patients may have abnormalities of their hands and feet in addition to abnormalities of the external ear and micrognathia. This condition is also dominantly inherited and should be easily recognised.

Genetic Factors	Incidence (approx) 50 %
Autosomal Dominant	Waardenburgs Syndrome (pigmentary anomalies) Klippel–Feil Syndrome Treacher Collins–Franceschetti Klein Alports Syndrome Otosclerosis

Autosomal Recessive	Without Associated Anomalies
	With Other Abnormalities
	  goitre
	  retinitis pigmentosa
	  E.C.G. abnormalities
	  partial albinism
	Galactosaemia
	Neurological Disease

X–Linked	Deafness c̄ Partial Albinism Hunters Disease
Environmental Factors	20 %

	Prenatal... infections.. Rubella
	                  Cytomegalovirus
	      ... drugs Toxoplasmosis

	Perinatal
	  Anoxia
	  Prematurity
	  Cerebral Haemorrhage
	  Kernicterus
	Postnatal... infections.. meningitis (TB)
	               encephalitis
	  ...trauma.... accidental
	          non accidental
	  ...drugs...... streptomycin

Unknown	30 %

Table 8.4 Causes of deafness.

In the majority of cases of congenital deafness, however, there will be no other associated defect and it is important to take a thorough history to exclude possible causes such as perinatal anoxia, intrauterine infections and other environmental causes. Where such

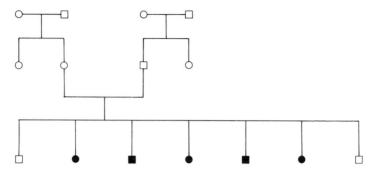

Fig. 8.6   Recessive deafness. Someone should have said something to the parents! Five profoundly deaf children in one family is exceptional but no-one ever discussed recessive inheritance with them.

factors can be proven then obviously the recurrence risk is low. When no such factors are apparent then it is very probable that the deafness is of genetic origin. When this group is further analysed it appears that the majority of patients have recessively inherited disease, probably as many as 75 per cent. A very small percentage, not more than five, are due to dominant or X-linked conditions and in the remainder it is impossible to show any definite causative factor, although a genetic aetiology is likely. In the family pedigree shown in Fig. 8.6, the disease is clearly recessively inherited with both parents having normal hearing and yet their children have proven congenital profound deafness. Hopefully, this is not something that would happen today. Families of this size are uncommon and most people would see the rearing of one or two deaf children as a sufficient burden to make them decide not to have further children. Genetic counselling in deafness is important and should attempt to ensure that the parents are made aware of any knowledge that is available and of the risks to further children. When both parents have normal hearing and there has been one child affected with non-specific deafness, the risk of a further affected child is between 1 in 6 and 1 in 10. Where one parent is deaf from unknown causes but has no affected relatives, then the risk to offspring will be about 1 in 30.

9
Ethical Issues and Future Developments

Ethical Issues

The corner stone of British medicine has been the development over the years of a very personal relationship between the nurse and her patients. In addition there has evolved a good working relationship between medical and nursing staff. There is generally an acceptance that both professions have patient interest as their main concern. In their traditional roles this would mean assessing a problem, attaching a diagnostic label where possible, ordering treatment and ensuring that the treatment was carried out. However, over the past few decades this traditional role of diagnostician and therapist, although still very necessary, has been subject to change and increasingly nurses and doctors have been forced to look at the possibility of disease prevention. For example, the association between cancer of the lung and cigarette smoking is now sufficiently well recognised for doctors and nurses to recommend to people that they should not smoke. This preventative type of medicine is still very much in its infancy and yet must become of increasing importance with the rocketing cost of delivering medical care. Advances in technology have also produced problems in which the standard therapist's role is no longer straightforward and nurses are constantly having to face situations where traditional guidelines are not available. In these, their involvement in patient management may to some extent be influenced by their moral, religious and cultural background. The ability to keep very handicapped children alive by artificial ventilation is an example of such a problem. Here the wishes of the parents, the views of the medical staff and the nursing staff may all be at variance and these matters are becoming of increasing public concern. In many such situations there is no simple answer and as has happened so often in the past it is necessary to rely on compassion, commonsense and professionalism.

Medicine, therefore, has had to adapt to the changing needs of our society. As some diseases become rare, others are highlighted and may present the profession with different problems requiring new solutions. Genetic counselling has now entered the medical field and some aspects of this work will undoubtedly present ethical difficulties for nurses, doctors and the public.

When we defined genetic counselling it was suggested that in many cases it could be seen as an extension of clinical medicine attempting to answer the question, 'What are the chances of it happening again?' It is interesting to speculate why it was that parents only rarely asked such questions of their medical attendants in the past. Presumably the public now have more medical awareness and there is less tendency to see the profession as unapproachable on these issues. In such a situation there would seem to be no ethical problem associated with the giving of the information required. However, in high risk conditions it is very important that such information is imparted sympathetically and with due regard to the consultand's intelligence and cultural background. In many instances, the risk will be such that a couple may well decide not to have further children. This is a very important decision for them to reach and restricted reproduction as a result of genetic counselling advice may produce emotional upset which should be anticipated. Factual information can, on occasions, be brutal and as far as possible it should be given in a non-directive way. For example, if the recurrence risk of a serious condition is high it would not be appropriate to say 'This is a very high risk and you must not, therefore, have any more children'. It is the parents' decision whether or not they have further children and the purpose of counselling is to make their decision an informed one. On occasions, parents at a loss as to what to do, may well ask the counselling staff what they would do in similar circumstances. None of us really know how we would respond in certain situations and this has to be stressed. However, where professional knowledge and experience points to an inevitable outcome, sympathetic direction may be appreciated. The genetic nurse's role in this common situation will be to act with compassion and to help the families and individuals come to terms with whatever decision they have made. This philosophy is adopted by the majority of genetic counselling services throughout the world.

There are, however, some situations in counselling work in which the doctor's and nurse's role is not as clear cut. For example, during a pedigree search a number of individuals may be identified who are at risk of a specific disease or of having affected children. Huntington's Chorea is a good example of such a disease. Sibs of affected patients have a risk of 50/50 of inheriting the gene and of developing the clinical manifestations at some time in their life. Their children in turn are also at risk of inheriting the gene. If the persons concerned have not come for advice, should they be told about the risk bearing in mind that we have no treatment for the disease and no means of identifying the pre-clinical carrier? There is no easy answer to this question. It would obviously be important to discuss the matter with the person's general practitioner as in other medical problems. In addition, some help may be available from relatives who have attended the clinic. In all cases, however, there has to be regard to the confidentiality of patient information and this is an important and complicating factor. In some situations it may be difficult to discuss an individual's problem even with a close family member. The experience from genetic counselling clinics would suggest that most consultands want more information even when it may be unpleasant. Very few individuals prefer not to be told the facts relating to their particular problem. This is unlikely to be an inevitable rule, however, and there will be recurrent problems of this sort. It is our practice to take advice from the family doctor and this is usually helpful. For example, if a person is reported to be of nervous disposition and an undue worrier there would probably be little gained from informing him that he was at risk of Huntington's Chorea. However, by withholding information one is constantly running the risk of being criticised. In most cases a sympathetic delivery of factual information should not produce too much emotional upset and the nurse normally has an important role in this situation. Each case must be assessed and managed individually. There must be adequate time for discussion with the people concerned and every effort must be made to ensure that the information is understood. It is important to accept that not everyone 'wants to know'. Having knowledge of their carrier status will upset some people and if they do not want to know then their wishes should be respected.

Large scale *screening programmes* could obviously multiply this special type of problem many-fold. It is possible to recognise certain populations at risk for various diseases and an example has already been quoted of Tay-Sach's Disease in the Ashkenazic Jewish population in America. The carriers of the responsible gene can be identified and the affected fetus diagnosed *in utero*. There is, therefore, a positive outcome to this screening procedure and it would be seen by many as beneficial to the at-risk population. When the Tay-Sach's screening programme was instituted in parts of North America very great efforts were made to inform high school children about the genetics of the disease. In addition the genetic counselling services enlisted the aid of the Rabbis and there was very wide discussion of the whole issue on television and in the press. There was, therefore, a very definite attempt to have an informed group of people and not to attempt screening a population unsure of the real nature of the problem. When a similar attempt was made to screen for sickle-cell disease and thalassaemia, some of the coloured population at risk felt that this was being made into a racial issue. The screening programme in this situation resulted in an increase in racial tension in the towns in which it was attempted. This emphasises the importance of the nurse and genetic counselling staff being very sensitive to the issues involved in this type of work.

In the identification of carriers in conditions such as Tay-Sach's Disease or thalassaemia, the couple may decide not to have children. This decision is reached on an informed basis and is very personal to them. However, when prenatal diagnostic tests are offered then further issues are involved. Interference with a pregnancy, with the possibility of termination of that pregnancy, does present moral and ethical issues to doctors, nurses and members of the public. There is a very strong anti-abortion lobby both in this country and elsewhere. There are now a number of societies whose aim is to protect the unborn child and these societies accept, as part of their role, the need to prevent abortion and to change the law on this procedure. This may be associated with religious beliefs in many instances and it is reasonable that people who have such views should be allowed to express them. Nevertheless, it is very difficult for those who criticise this new medical development to understand the issues if they have not been personally involved. It would be difficult to justify withholding prenatal testing for those couples who would clearly benefit from it. On the other hand this does not morally justify the procedure to those who object to the whole approach. When these issues are discussed with individuals at risk they usually welcome the help that can be offered by amniocentesis and prenatal diagnosis.

Genetic counselling staff and obstetricians involved in this work need to be aware of the emotional problems associated with the procedure and with the termination of pregnancy. It is important that a woman should not feel she has been forced to have prenatal diagnosis and nothing should be done during pregnancy without consent of both husband and wife. Full discussion is mandatory and sufficient time must be available so that the families concerned may ask questions and voice some of their anxieties. We have already considered those conditions which can be diagnosed prenatally. Perhaps the most difficult problems are with X-linked disease where the only help that may be available is to determine fetal sex and to terminate a male pregnancy if that is the family's wish. This was never a very satisfactory way of dealing with the problem and intrauterine diagnosis of the disease is a much more positive approach.

Many members of the public see genetic counselling and its effects as an attempt to breed only healthy stock. Such a breeding policy is of course fully accepted in veterinary work and in human populations is the science of *eugenics*. Unfortunately over the past 50 years there have been attempts by dictators and political regimes to obliterate various population groups. This has naturally resulted in many people finding any discussion on eugenics distasteful. However, the natural progression of any society must be towards improvement and most of us would wish to see the disappearance of many serious and disabling genetic diseases. The fact that many people still react emotively to this type of discussion should be appreciated. Nurses and doctors working in clinical genetics would, in the majority of cases, see their role as helping individual families. They would not see it as being involved in any eugenic practices in the broader sense. However, strictly speaking all in this field will have to accept that they are involved in some form of eugenic practice. Our aim should be to ensure that individual and family interests are always more important than the interests of society as a whole.

Another issue which has produced widespread critical comment from some members of the public is *genetic engineering*. This is the name given to techniques by which an organism's genetic constitution can be altered. To date this has only been done with viruses and bacteria and although it may have application for diseases in man, it may be some time before this will be possible. Unfortunately, the impression has been given that genetic engineering in individuals is just around the corner and this has produced criticism from many people anxious about this type of work. A number of scientific writers have expressed very great concern about its dangers and some of these fears may be justified. Like many other scientific techniques genetic engineering needs to be carefully monitored. Basically the procedure involves adding virus DNA to alter the DNA of a bacterium; the genetic constitution of the bacterium is thereby changed. It is hoped that a similar approach could be applied to human disease, for example to make good the deficiency of a particular enzyme. However, to accomplish this it would first of all be necessary to locate the abnormal gene locus responsible for the enzyme and the DNA molecular chain would then have to split at that point. This might be possible by the use of endonucleases which are enzymes present in most bacterial species and are known to be capable of disrupting the DNA chain. It would then be necessary to incorporate a new portion of DNA containing the required coded information into the original molecule. The replacement DNA with the appropriate genetic information could be produced by the action of an enzyme known as reverse transcriptase. This is obtained from certain viruses and would allow DNA to be manufactured from the RNA template: a reversal of the usual flow of genetic information. This is a formidable task and probably not practicable in man for some years.

Concern has also been expressed about the possible increase in deleterious genes as a result of improvements in the treatment of patients with inherited disease. Although this will alter 'the gene pool' the change will be slow and any effects gradual. Meantime research continues and may eventually provide a means of preventing some of these diseases.

Recommendations for Future Developments

Genetic counselling is now an accepted and established service in most medically developed countries in the world. There is need, however, for further expansion of the services to meet the increasing demand by the public for this type of advice.

It is reasonable to assume that this trend will continue. This has been the case in North America and although the reasons are complex it is unlikely that any different pattern will emerge here. Public and professional interest has been stimulated by increasing discussion on various aspects of genetics on television, in the press and by vocal patient groups and vigorous national organisations. Over the years enthusiastic advocates of the service both in Great Britain and North America, have convincingly demonstrated its application to many patient problems. Perhaps more than any other factor, interest in genetic counselling has been stimulated by the advent of prenatal diagnostic techniques in the management of neural tube and other disorders. Despite the ethical and medico-legal implications inherent in this work it would be difficult to withhold it from families requesting help.

Congenital and genetic disorders now constitute a considerable proportion of the total load of disease in our community. In most if not all of these cases counselling could be considered appropriate. The community also contains a considerable genetic load composed of patients under the care of orthopaedic surgeons, neurologists, physicians and ophthalmologists. Although referrals from these sources are gradually increasing there is evidence that the profession as a whole is slow to refer patients with inherited disease to counselling clinics. Many patients at high risk are given no information about the genetic implications of their disease. Hopefully this situation will be altered by education of graduate doctors in the relevance of genetics to their patients' problems.

The storage of genetic information presents a number of difficult problems. There is need for a system which will allow for ease and reliability of operation as well as for constant updating of information. Confidentiality of the case material is important and some means of ensuring this essential. Finally it should simplify recall of data and facilitate research work. Computer registration of the information may be one possible solution. Several centres already use such a system and despite the obvious concern, confidentiality can be greater than that guaranteed by current hospital record systems. In addition computer registration could benefit record linkage systems, bringing together information from centres throughout the country.

Although most medical centres in the United Kingdom now include some teaching in clinical genetics in the undergraduate curriculum, there is little doubt that the time allocated is often inadequate. Meantime there are continuing advances in the application of genetics to clinical practice. It is important that future doctors have a training which will help them meet the community's medical needs and this seems bound to include more awareness of the importance of disease prevention in addition to disease therapy. There is currently a disproportionate allocation of financial resources to increasingly expensive technology both in the treatment and investigation of patient illness.

In addition to the need for future doctors to be more aware of genetic principles it would seem important that boys and girls leaving secondary education should have some understanding of the practical implications of genetics for their lives. This may mean some modification of the standard biology course taught in most schools. This is an important and practical aspect of education which needs further research.

Genetic counselling and prenatal diagnostic services are here to stay. However, we do need to know more about the effects of such services; not only on the parents, but also on other children in the family. This would be best done by prospective studies of families attending the clinics. In addition we need further information about those factors which influence consultands' decisions and the effectiveness of counselling. Significant advances in the management of many diseases await further basic biological knowledge. Much of this is likely to be related to the science of genetics and research in this field will continue to expand.

As a nation we have still not discussed many of the issues raised by

Fig. 8.7   We are not at this stage yet and not likely to be for some time! In the past mothers assessed their daughters' suitors by inquiring about their financial prospects. This was an old fashioned way of asking the same question as the minister in the cartoon. If the suitor's future was promising it was a fair bet he had a good complement of genes!

this type of work. So far public debate on prenatal diagnosis has been scanty, in comparison to that which has taken place in the United States of America over the past ten years. Nevertheless, the prevention of disease, including inherited disease, is a reasonable aim for any society and this inevitably produces medical, ethical and legal problems. Individual counselling centres will find their own solution to many of these issues, but sooner or later agreement on a national scale will have to be reached and universal guidelines adopted. The future is now and as always is very exciting. The aim of medicine should be to ensure that all of us, nurses and doctors, adapt to the changing needs of the community in which we work.

Glossary

allele   One of two or more alternative forms of a gene.

aneuploid   A chromosome number which is not an exact multiple of the haploid number, e.g. trisomy or monosomy.

ascertainment   Identification of individuals and families with hereditary disease.

autosome   Any chromosome other than the X- or Y-chromosome.

Barr Body   A densely-staining chromatin mass within the nuclear membrane of cells in the normal female.

carrier   A carrier of genetic disease may transmit the responsible gene or chromosomal abnormality but normally does not show any evidence of the disease.

centromere   The small junction area between the two arms of a chromosome.

chromosome   Structures within the nucleus, containing the genes and composed of DNA and protein.

chromatid   The two daughter strands of a chromosome still joined at the centromere.

codon   A sequence of three nucleotides which codes for an aminoacid or has a regulatory function in the decoding progress.

concordant   A term used to indicate that both twins have a given trait.

congenital   Characteristic present at birth, either genetic or environmental in origin.

consanguinity   Descent from common ancestors, i.e. blood relatives.

cytogenetics   Study of chromosomes.

cytoplasm   Protoplasm of cell in which is situated the nucleus, the ribosomes and other bodies.

deletion   Loss of a part of a chromosome.

dermatoglyphics   The study of skin ridge patterns on the hands and feet.

diploid   The situation in which body cells contain two sets of chromosomes. The diploid number in man is 46.

discordant   A term used to indicate that twins do not share the same trait.

dizygote   Twins produced from two ova by different sperms.

dominant   Normally used to define a trait expressed in individuals who are heterozygous for a particular gene, i.e. when it is present in single dose.

euploid   A number which is a specific multiple of the normal haploid or diploid number.

gamete   A sperm or ovum containing the haploid number of chromosomes. In man 23.

gene   A section of DNA coded for a specific group of nucleotides.

gene locus   Site of a gene and its allelle on a chromosome.

gene pool   The total genetic complement of a generation.

haploid   The situation in which there is a single set of unpaired chromosomes, i.e. in the gametes.

hemizygous   The genotype of a male with an X-linked trait.

heterozygous   Having two different alleles at the same locus on paired chromosomes.

homologous chromosomes   Chromosomes which pair at meiosis and contain identical loci.

homozygous   Having identical alleles at a given locus on a pair of chromosomes.

karyotype   Photographic demonstration of chromosomes.

locus   Position of a gene on a chromosome.

meiosis   Type of cell division with halving of the somatic chromosome number.

mitosis   Type of cell division resulting in a constant chromosome number.

monosomy   Loss of one of a pair of chromosomes.

monozygotic   Identical twins from a single fertilised ovum.

mosaic   A person with two or more karyotypes in their cell population.

mutation   Alteration in gene structure or chromosomal complement.

non-disjunction Failure of two homologous chromosomes to separate into daughter cells at meiosis.

nucleotide Chemical consisting of a sugar, a phosphate and a base.

penetrance Implies the ability of a gene to produce some changes in the genotype with some resultant change in the phenotype.

phenotype The appearance of an individual reflecting the underlying genotype and other factors.

polyploid Any multiple of the haploid or diploid number of chromosomes.

proband An individual who directs attention to the family pedigree.

recessive A trait which is produced in individuals who are homozygous for a particular gene – have a 'double dose'.

ribosomes Small cellular particles composed of RNA and protein.

sex-linked Genes which are carried on the sex chromosomes.

teratogen Any agent thought to cause congenital abnormalities.

transcription Transfer of genetic information from DNA to mRNA.

translocation Transfer of one chromosome or portion of chromosome to another. It may also be to another location on the same chromosome.

translation The conversion of information on the mRNA to protein.

trisomy Three instead of normal two chromosomes of any pair.

unifactorial Resulting from a single gene with major effect.

X-linked Genes carried on an X-chromosome.

zygote Fertilised ovum. A new individual.

Recommended Books

Emery, Alan E. H. (1979), *Elements of Medical Genetics*. 4th edn. Edinburgh: Churchill Livingstone.

Hilton, B., Callahan, D., Harris, M., Condliffe, P and Berkley, B. (1975), *Ethical Issues in Human Genetics*. New York and London: Plenum Press.

Kelly, Patricia T. (1977), *Dealing with Dilemma*. New York: Heidelberg Science Library, Springer-Verlag.

McKusick, V. A. (1978), *Mendelian Inheritance in Man*. Baltimore, Ohio: The Johns Hopkins University Press. *(for reference only)*

Salmon, Michael A. (1978), *Developmental Defects and Syndromes*. Aylesbury: HM+M Publishers Ltd. *(for reference only)*

Siggers, D. C. (1978), *Prenatal Diagnosis of Genetic Disease*. Oxford: Blackwell Scientific Publications Ltd.

Stevenson, A. C. and Clare Davidson, B.C. (1976), *Genetic Counselling*. London: William Heinemann Medical Books Ltd.

Appendix A

Dear

Re: GENETIC COUNSELLING CLINIC

You may already know the sort of help that can be given at the Genetic Counselling Clinic. If you are not clear about the work we do the following information may be helpful.

Families, or individuals, come to the clinic for various reasons, e.g. a couple may have had a child with a serious abnormality at birth and wish to know the chances of this happening again. Other people come to us wondering if a condition which is in the family might be handed down to their children. Often we see people suffering from handicaps such as deafness or even families concerned about frequent miscarriages or still-births. In all these situations medical facts are essential and so also are details of the family tree or pedigree. It would be helpful, therefore, if you could manage to obtain as much information as possible about your family background before coming to the clinic. Many people find it easier to list details of relatives, with information about age, past or present illnesses and cause of death where these are known.

You will have an appointment time allocated and normally you should be prepared to spend at least an hour on your first visit, but less on subsequent visits.

If, for any reason, you are unable to attend for your appointment, would you please contact the clinic secretary on the number and extension below. This is most important because non-attendance results in wastage of valuable clinic time.

If there are any further queries please do not hesitate to telephone the secretary.

Telephone number.

Yours sincerely,

Genetic Counselling Service

Appendix B

Mr and Mrs J. Smith,
4 Walk Way,
Nottingham

Dear Mr and Mrs Smith,

I felt it would be helpful to review for you some of the facts we discussed when you attended the genetic counselling clinic on 1st January 1977. Down's Syndrome (or mongolism) is common and occurs in approximately 1 in 750 births. It is, therefore, a problem facing many parents throughout the world. As was explained it normally results from an abnormality of those structures we call chromosomes. These are present in all the body cells and are composed of genes, the units of heredity. These cannot be seen but chromosomes can be examined under the microscope and the picture shown to you and your husband is called a karyotype. This confirmed that your daughter, Gillian, has three chromosomes of No. 21 instead of the normal two. This is called trisomy 21 and it is this which produces all the features of Down's Syndrome.

The alteration in the number of chromosomes normally results from an accident in cell division before fertilisation and can occur in either mother or father. This produces an egg or sperm with two No. 21 chromosomes instead of just one. When fertilisation occurs an individual is formed who has three instead of two No. 21 chromosomes. This is the situation in over 90 per cent of all children with this condition but you may hear of an occasional child with Down's Syndrome who has a different chromosomal derangement. This may be a translocation or mosaicism. Neither of these two apply to your child or yourselves.

We do not know why there should be unequal sharing of chromosomes but it is important that both of you appreciate that this was not something over which you have any control and so no-one is at fault. The chromosomal analysis performed on both of you was completely normal.

The important fact for the future is that there is only a very slight risk of such an accident occurring again. Mother's age is important in this respect and the risk we quoted to you is not greater than

1 in 100.

Most couples who attend our clinic would see this risk as reassuring. Unfortunately, as mother's age increases so does the risk of Down's

Syndrome and it would be sensible, therefore, if you decide to have another baby not to wait too long. The risk is appreciably greater when mother's age exceeds 40.

Many couples who have had a child with Down's Syndrome request amniocentesis in subsequent pregnancies. We discussed the details of this and in your case with such a low risk the test would be primarily for reassurance. The fluid obtained by the obstetrician contain's baby's skin cells and these can be grown and their chromosomes examined. This prenatal testing is now very common and you will probably realise that we will know baby's sex before birth. Some parents like to be given this information early in pregnancy and others do not, the matter is left entirely to you. Normally amniocentesis is a very safe procedure but I did explain that there is a slight risk of a miscarriage, about 1 in 100 (the same risk as having another child with Down's Syndrome). Some other minor problems may occur such as slight bleeding but this is normally something which is very brief and your obstetrician will normally explain these details to you. Unfortunately, it is necessary to repeat the test in about 1 in 20 patients. This is because the cells have not grown properly or because fluid has not been obtained. It is best that you know about this possibility but hopefully it will not apply to you. I would like to stress that you can decide not to have this test. It would only be done with your full agreement.

I have already written to your family doctor and a copy of the letter has been forwarded to the obstetrician who looked after you in your last pregnancy. Everyone, therefore, will be very familiar with your background if you do become pregnant again.

I hope that this brief summary is useful to you. If there are further facts you would like to discuss we would be very pleased to try and help and you have the telephone number of the service.

Yours sincerely,

Genetic Counselling Service

Index

Homozygote, 27, 37
Hunter's Syndrome, 120–1
Huntington's Chorea, 1, 23, 25,
    32, 72, 83–5, 141
Hurler's Syndrome, 120–1
Hydrocephalus, 6, 69, 93
21-Hydroxylase, 85
Hypophosphataemic vitamin D
    resistant rickets, 45
Hypospadias, 95, 96

Immunological defence
    mechanism, 40
Incontinentia pigmenti, 45–6
Information storage, 79, 145
Inheritance patterns, 27–71

Karyotype, 5, 9, 14, 15, 46–8
Karyotype X0, 57
Kidney abnormalities, 3
Klinefelter's Syndrome, 58, 59, 63.
    115, 117
Krabbe's leucodystrophy, 119

Lactose, 25
Laryngomalacia, 65
Laurence-Moon-Biedl Syndrome,
    128, 134
Lyon hypothesis, 45

Marfan's Syndrome, 9, 71, 95
Meckel's Syndrome, 71, 111
Meiosis, 18, 54
Mendel, Gregor, 28
Mendelian disease, 28
Meningomyelocele, 69

Mental retardation, 6, 50, 98,
    124–31
Messenger RNA, 20
Metabolic disorders, 119–23
Metabolism, 38
Metachromatic leucodystrophy,
    119
Microcephaly, 6, 128–9
Mitosis, 17
Monosomy-X, 57
Morbidity changes, 1–3
Mortality changes, 1–3
Mosaicism, 115–18, 127
Mucopolysaccharidoses, 6
Multifactorial diseases, 10
Multifactorial inheritance, 66–71,
    93–7
Muscular dystrophy, 90–3
Mutations, 13, 28, 33

Neural tube defects, 3, 68, 109–11
Neurofibromatosis, 31, 32
Non-disjunction, 55
Noonan's Syndrome, 103

Ophthalmic nurse, 133–5

Paediatric nurse, 74
Pedigrees, 23–6
    symbols used, 23
Penetrance, 33
Phenocopy, 12
Phenotype, 27
Phenylalanine hydroxylase, 38
Phenylketonuria, 6, 38, 125
Physically handicapped school
    leaver, 131–3
Phytohaemagglutinin, 47